W9-BMQ-252

201
Fat-Burning
Recipes

by **Cathi Graham**

CATHI GRAHAM'S *Fresh Start*
METABOLISM PROGRAM

PUBLISHED BY

Fresh Start Metabolism Programs Ltd.

EIGHTH PRINTING

Design and page composition:
HOLE-IN-THE-WALL COMMUNICATIONS, VANCOUVER

Canadian Cataloguing in Publication Data

Graham, Cathi, 1957-

     201 fat-burning recipes

     ISBN 1-895292-34-4

1. Reducing diets – Recipes.   2. Lipids – Metabolism.
I. Title.

RM222.2.G72 1993   613.2'8   C93-098219-3

Printed and Produced in Canada by:
Centax Books, A Division of PW Group
1150 Eighth Avenue, Regina, Saskatchewan, Canada S4R 1C9
(306) 525-2304   FAX (306) 757-2439
E-mail: centax@printwest.com   www.centaxbooks.com

How I Lost 186 Pounds

If diets worked, you wouldn't read about a new miracle weight-loss scheme every week in your favorite magazine. If diets worked, a whopping 80 million Americans wouldn't be overweight. And if diets really worked, you wouldn't be reading this right now.

The Fresh Start Metabolism Program™ is not a diet. In fact, its premise is that if you want to permanently lose weight, you must throw away the diet mentality forever.

And it works. How can I say that so confidently, you ask? Well, in the early eighties I weighed a whopping 326 pounds (on a 5' 4" frame) – and I was at the end of my rope. I had been on every diet known to man, only to gain more and more weight. Then I made the best decision of my life. I threw away the diet mentality and embarked on a research quest to learn everything I could about metabolism, the Glycemic Index and motivational techniques. These concepts turned out to be the answers I'd always been looking for – but could never find.

Everything I learned I tested on myself. And sure enough, the pounds started to slip away. **Within 18 months I reduced 186 lbs.** I have kept the weight off ever since.

If it worked for me, I knew it could work for countless others. So, I put all of my energy and passion into developing The Fresh Start Metabolism Program™. Over the years, I've helped thousands of men and women who have been empowered by and reached their goal weight with my program.

Before I get into my passion – talking about the Fresh Start program, let me tell you what's in store for you with the **201 Fat-Burning Recipes** book. Most of the recipes are easy to prepare and all of them are delicious. Each recipe is calculated for servings, calories and fat grams, and at the beginning of each chapter, there is information on the specific benefits of each type of food.

What does the Fresh Start Metabolism Program™ have to offer? Fresh Start is not a diet – it's a lifestyle. It introduces the revolutionary concept of thermogenic foods and the Glycemic Index, which help dieters find out why rice cakes, pasta and carrots won't help them lose weight, but how apples, yogurt and 20 other foods will help them stay full and satisfied. I also reveal 25 different foods, including salsa and hot mustard, that can actually burn fat!

The Fresh Start Metabolism Program™ also explains the benefits of the Glycemic Index. For instance, have you ever noticed that after eating certain meals you feel hungrier than before you ate? The Glycemic Index is the key to explaining why this happens.

The Glycemic Index is the rate at which foods break down to be released as glucose into the bloodstream. Depending on their effect on insulin production, foods can be labeled high, moderate or low on the Glycemic Index.

To give you a summary of the program, it's unlike any other diet out there! My program helps the frustrated, diet-battle-weary person learn a new way of balanced eating. At the same time, I reveal that some carbohydrates, whether fat-laden, calorie-reduced or fat-free, can actually make you fatter, and keep you that way. I teach you how to use the Glycemic Index to your benefit, and how to release yourself from the diet mentality forever.

Fresh Start also includes two other very important components – a thorough look at the emotional roots of eating and the role of fun, light activity. I teach people how to uncover the emotional link to their eating patterns, how to boost their self-esteem, and how to stay motivated over the long term.

After years of giving seminars and receiving feedback from my clients, I know that people are tired of dieting. They're looking for satisfying food, loving support and a good dose of humor. That is exactly what the Fresh Start Metabolism Program™ offers you. It includes videos, audio cassettes and an informative, easy-to-use manual, plus meal plans, restaurant guides and newsletters.

Over the years, the Fresh Start Metabolism Program™ has grown from a one-person program to a multi-faceted corporation, but the basic premise has always remained the same: **To help people free themselves from the diet mentality forever, and find happiness, health and peace of mind.**

To find out more about the Fresh Start Metabolism Program™, please call 1-800-663-7374. To learn more about other Fresh Start tools, please refer to the last page of this cookbook.

Dedication

This book is dedicated to my mom, Mary Mullin, who believed in me fat or slim. It is also dedicated to over eight-five percent of North America who, like myself, have struggled, or continue to struggle to make peace with themselves and the scales. I know this book will help you successfully begin your journey.

Enjoy your transformation . . .

Cathi

Table of Contents

Remember...

...Everything in life is a compromise, and cooking is no exception.
If you take ALL the sugar, fat and salt out of food, people won't eat it.
I urge you to make only small changes initially. You'll be surprised at
what little differences will do for your figure!

Herb & Spice Chart

ANISE	Fish, shellfish
BASIL	Fish, poultry, tomatoes, vegetables
BAY LEAF	Meats, fish
CAPERS	Fish, salads, tomatoes
CARAWAY	Meats, cabbage, turnips
CARDAMOM	Sweet potatoes
CAYENNE	"Hot" – any food
CELERY SEED	Cabbage, tomato, potatoes
CHERVIL	Fish, shellfish, green salads
CHIVES	Fish, baked potatoes, salads
CILANTRO	Ground meat, beans, Mexican foods
CINNAMON	Pork, fruits
CLOVE	Pork
CUMIN	Ground meat, cabbage
DILL	Fish, shellfish, meats, salads
FENNEL	Chicken, fish, shellfish
GINGER	Fish, shellfish, poultry, stir fry dishes
HORSERADISH	Fish, shellfish, all meats
MARJORAM	Lamb, poultry, vegetables
MINT	Lamb, beans, peas, fruit
MUSTARD	Beets, adds life to most foods
NUTMEG	Vegetables (especially pumpkin)
OREGANO	Ground meat, fish, tomatoes
PAPRIKA	Fish, salads, potatoes
PARSLEY	Fish, meats, poultry, salad, vegetables
ROSEMARY	Beef, lamb, pork, chicken, vegetables
SAFFRON	Fish, shellfish
SAGE	Fish, shellfish, pork, veal
SAVORY	Lentils, beans, fish, shellfish, ground meat, poultry
TARRAGON	Meats, poultry, tomatoes
THYME	Clams, fish, poultry, tomatoes
TURMERIC	Fish, shellfish, chicken, noodles, pasta, rice
SPIKE	Salads, stews, potatoes, dips, popcorn
MRS DASH™	(14 herbs and spices) salt substitute

Scrumptious Salads

Tips:

1. Cut down on fat in creamy salad dressing, but not the taste by mixing it with plain low-fat yogurt and water if desired.

2. Be sure to wear rubber gloves when handling hot peppers or wash hands thoroughly after handling. Skin, especially around the eyes, is very sensitive to the oil from peppers.

Chili Chicken

Ingredients

1 pound chicken cutlets (boneless, skinless, chicken breasts)
2 Tbsp. orange juice, freshly
squeezed

1 tsp. chili powder, or to taste
¼ tsp. ground cumin
Dash ground cloves

1 scallion, minced
1 shallot, peeled and smashed
through a garlic press
4 Tbsp. minced fresh parsley
1 stalk celery (leaves, too),
minced
¼ cup low-fat plain yogurt
1 Tbsp. lemon juice, freshly
squeezed

Soft tortillas or lettuce petals

Yield: 6 servings

Directions

Trim the chicken of visible fat. If
pieces aren't of equal thickness,
lay between two sheets of
waxed paper and pound with a
meat mallet until equal. Place
the pieces around the outer
edge of a 9-inch glass pie plate
and sprinkle with orange juice.
cover with vented plastic wrap
and microwave on high until
cooked through, about 4½ minutes, rotating and turning the
pieces midway. Let stand 5 minutes, or refrigerate before
serving. The chicken may be
used in any chicken salad recipe
you wish.

Combine chili powder, cumin
and cloves in a small bowl and
microwave on high, until heated
through and fragrant, about 1
minute.

CONTINUED NEXT PAGE

Calories and fat without tortillas.

Cal 199   Fat 5.2 g

Scoop spices into a large bowl along with scallion, parsley, celery, yogurt, and lemon juice.

Using your fingers, shred the chicken into bite-size pieces (it's easier done along the grain). Toss well with the yogurt mixture. Serve slightly chilled with tortillas or lettuce for rolling.

Eight More
Quick Chicken Salads

Great with whole wheat pitas!

*All with 2 cups of cooked chicken or turkey cut into cubes.

Yield: 6 servings

Light Salsa 134 Cal/4 g Fat
Toss 2 to 4 tablespoons salsa with 2 tablespoons light mayo; stir in chicken. Spoon onto shredded lettuce.

Creamy Caesar 132 Cal/4 g Fat
Stir chicken with ¼ cup creamy light caesar dressing, 2 thinly sliced green onions and ground black pepper. Sprinkle lightly with parmesan cheese and bacon bits (optional).

Tarragon Yogurt 125 Cal/3 g Fat
Blend 3 tablespoons plain yogurt with 1 teaspoon finely grated lemon peel and ½ tsp. tarragon. Stir in chicken. (Optional: dash of onion powder and 1 sliced celery stalk).

Double Mustard 150 Cal/3 g Fat
Blend ½ cup light mayo with 1 teaspoon each of Dijon and honey mustard. Stir in chicken and ½ julienned red or green pepper.

Honey-Lime 139 Cal/3 g Fat
Blend ¼ cup light sour cream with 1 teaspoon liquid honey and grated peel of 1 lime. Stir in 1 cup cubed honeydew or cantaloupe melon and chicken.

Simply Spice 138 Cal/4 g Fat
Blend ½ teaspoon cumin and a pinch of cayenne into 3 tablespoons light mayo. Toss with chicken.

Tangy Blue 201 Cal/3 g Fat
Toss chicken with 2 cups cooked whole wheat pasta, 1 chopped red-skinned apple and ¼ cup light blue cheese dressing.

Curried Chutney 142 Cal/4 g Fat
Stir 1 Tbsp. mango chutney and ¼ teaspoon curry into ¼ cup light mayo. Toss with chicken

Barley and Chicken Salad

Ingredients

8 oz. low-fat plain yogurt
1 small garlic clove, chopped
2 Tbsp. soya sauce
½ tsp. ground ginger

3 cups cooked pearl barley
½ cup green peas (frozen)
1 red sweet pepper, cut in strips
¾ lb. cooked chicken, chopped
9 oz. water chestnuts, drained

Directions

In large salad bowl combine the yogurt, garlic, soya sauce and ginger.

Stir in remaining ingredients. Mix well and chill a minimum of 2 hours. Serve on a bed of red lettuce or other salad greens. Sprinkle with lemon juice if desired.

Yield: 6 servings

This recipe submitted by Valerie Morris.

Cal 240   Fat 1 g

SALADS

Creamy Fruit Salad

Ingredients

1½ cups Red Delicious apples, diced
1 cup banana, sliced
1 cup orange sections, seeded, reserve juice
½ cup green grapes, seedless
1 8-ounce container low-fat flavoured yogurt
Cinnamon

Directions

Combine apple, banana, orange sections and grapes in medium-size bowl. Toss well with reserved orange juice and yogurt.
Sprinkle with cinnamon if desired

Yield: 4 servings

Cal 133   Fat 1 g

Mediterranean Salad

Ingredients

¾ cup diced cucumber
½ cup diced tomato
⅓ cup chopped scallion
2 Tbsp. chopped green bell pepper

1½ tsp. olive oil
1 tsp. red wine vinegar or cider vinegar
Freshly ground black pepper, to taste.

Directions

Combine vegetables.

When ready to serve, toss well with oil, vinegar and pepper.

Yield: 1 serving

Cal 112   Fat 7 g

Chili Bean Salad

Great for lunch-time sandwiches!

Ingredients

¾ cup cooked (or canned)
   drained kidney or pinto beans
3 Tbsp. chopped celery
2 tsp. light mayonnaise
1 tsp. cider vinegar
¼ - 1 tsp. chili powder
Dash of onion powder
Freshly ground black pepper, to
   taste.

Directions

Combine all ingredients in small
bowl, mix well.

**Yield: Approx. 1 cup
      (3 sandwiches)**

Cal 68   Fat 1 g

Middle East Salad

Ingredients

1 large eggplant

½ cup cooked Kasha (wheat)
¼ cup green pepper, chopped
¼ cup parsley, chopped fine
¼ cup lemon juice
½ cup green onion, chopped
2 tomatoes, chopped
1 garlic clove, chopped fine
½ tsp. salt (optional)
½ tsp. lemon zest

Directions

Bake whole eggplant at 400°
for 1 hour. When slightly cooled,
peel and chop.

Combine all ingredients in salad
bowl. May be served at room
temperature or chill 1 hour
before serving.

Yield: 6 servings

*This recipe submitted by Valerie
Morris.*

Cal 44   Fat "tr"

Coleslaw

This fibre-rich colourful coleslaw is best made a day ahead as the flavour is enhanced as it marinates.

Ingredients
....

5 carrots
3 cups cauliflower florets

12 cups finely shredded red and
  green cabbage
1 cup chopped green onions
  (about 8)
½ cup chopped fresh parsley
⅓ cup granulated sugar

¾ cup cider vinegar
⅓ cup oil
1 Tbsp. dried tarragon
2 tsp. basil
1 tsp. salt (if desired)
Dash pepper

Yield: 8 servings
....

Directions
....

Cut carrots into 2 x 1/8 inch (5 cm x 3 mm) strips. You should have about 2 cups julienned carrots. In pot of boiling salted water, cook carrots and cauliflower for 2 to 3 minutes or until tender-crisp. Rinse under cold running water; pat dry.

In large bowl, combine carrots, cauliflower, cabbage, onions, parsley and sugar; let stand, covered, in refrigerator for at least 1 hour or up to 8 hours.

In small saucepan, bring to boil vinegar, oil, tarragon, basil, salt and pepper. Pour over salad and toss. Cover and let marinate in refrigerator for at least 2 hours or up to 1 day.

Cal 175

Fat 10 g

Vegetable Medley

Ingredients

2 large purple onions, sliced
   paper thin
1 medium cauliflower, broken
   into tiny flowerets
4 large green peppers, seeded
   and cut into thin strips, 1½
   inches long
(Can also use carrots, julienned;
   broccoli flowerets, fresh mushrooms, cut thinly)

1 Tbsp. wine vinegar
2/3 cup low-cal oil & vinegar
   dressing
1 tsp. salt substitute
2 tsp. dry mustard
Dash black pepper
2 cloves garlic, crushed
2 tsp. chopped parsley
2 tsp. chopped chives OR green
   onions
1 tsp. dried leaf chervil
Pinch dried leaf tarragon

Yield: 6 servings

Directions

Cook onions, cauliflower and
green peppers separately in
boiling salted water. Each will
take about 10 minutes. Combine
vegetables in a large bowl.

Put all remaining ingredients in a
jar with a tight lid and shake to
blend well. Pour over the hot
vegetables and toss lightly with
a fork. Cool, then cover with
transparent wrap and chill.
Serve as salad.

Cal 113   Fat 7 g

Turkey-Apple Salad

*Unusual & very tasty! Great in
the summer season.*

Ingredients

1 ¼ cups cooked turkey, cubed
2 cups celery, diced
2 cups Granny Smith apples,
  unpeeled, cored and diced
¼ cup raisins

2 Tbsp. light mayonnaise
2 Tbsp. low-fat yogurt
¼ tsp. nutmeg
¼ tsp. cinnamon
Salt and pepper to taste

Low-fat grated Cheddar cheese,
  (optional)

Directions

In a large bowl, combine turkey,
celery, apples and raisins.

In a small bowl, combine mayonnaise, yogurt, nutmeg and
cinnamon. Fold into turkey mixture. Season to taste.

Serve on crisp lettuce leaves and
garnish lightly with grated low-
fat Cheddar cheese if desired.

Yield: 6 servings

Cal 157   Fat 1.5 g

Curried Turkey and Pecan Salad

Ingredients

2½ cups chopped cooked turkey breast
2 medium apples, chopped
½ cup no-salt pecans

⅓ cup light salad dressing or mayonnaise
2 Tbsp. prepared mustard
½ cup low-fat yogurt
1 Tbsp. curry powder

⅓ cup chopped fresh parsley
2 Tbsp. grated onion

Yield: 6 servings

Directions

In a large bowl, combine turkey, apples and pecans

In a small bowl, combine salad dressing, mustard, yogurt, and curry powder. Mix dressing with turkey mixture.

Stir in parsley and onion.

Cal 269   Fat 12 g

Tofu, Broccoli and Egg Salad

Ingredients

8 oz. firm tofu, pressed in ½"
   cubes
4 hard-cooked eggs, shelled and
   sliced or chopped
1 cup broccoli flowerets
½ cup celery, chopped
2 Tbsp. green pepper, chopped
2 Tbsp. green onion, chopped
1 Tbsp. light mayonnaise
2 tsp. lemon juice
1 tsp. mustard powder
¼ tsp. garlic powder
¼ tsp. dill weed
Salt and pepper to taste (optional)

Directions

Mix all ingredients together in a
large covered container. Chill at
least 30 minutes or up to 1 day
in refrigerator. Serve on crisp lettuce leaves.

Yield: 2 servings

CHAPTER 2

Soup's On!

Soups

1. Sunshine Soup
2. Creamy Butternut Squash Soup
3. Yam Soup
4. Sweet Potato Soup
5. Minestrone Soup
6. 5-Bean Minestrone
7. My Famous Split Pea Soup
8. Lentil Soup
9. Hearty Soup with Rice
10. Cabbage Patch Soup
11. Beans & Barley Soup
12. Mixed-Bean Gumbo
13. Corn Chowder
14. New Potato Chowder
15. Old-Style Chunky Chicken Soup
16. Chicken Cheddar Soup
17. Speedy Gazpacho
18. Tooty-Fruity Soup
19. Festive Tomato Soup

Sauces

1. Italian Tomato Sauce (variations) Spanish/Mexican/Chunky
2. Spaghetti Sauce
3. Low Fat Gravy
4. Low-Cal Tartar Sauce
5. Tofu Sauce for Chicken, Seafood or Vegetables

Dips

1. Hot and Spicy Cheese Dip
2. White-Bean Dip
3. Low-Cal Sour Cream Dip
4. Veggie Dip
5. Cheese Spread

Soup Tips

Soups are an excellent Fat Burner. They are a great defence against overeating. Soups can go beyond simply adding no burden of fat to your system. They possess certain special properties to help promote weight loss. A study by Dr. John Foreyt, of Bayloc College of Medicine, found that people consuming a bowl of soup before lunch and dinner lost more weight than dieters who didn't; and that the more soup they ate the more they lost. Soup eaters tend to keep the weight off also.

Eat soup with a slice of high fibre bread or whole grain flat crackers, and some fruit and you'll have plenty of energy to keep you going through the rest of the day. Include soup in your weekly menu, at least twice. Serve for a satisfying dinner with a side salad and a few crackers. So ... Soups On!

Sunshine Soup

Ingredients

½ head cauliflower, separated
   into flowerets
2 large onions, chopped
3 large carrots, chopped
4 stalks celery, chopped
1 medium zucchini, chopped
1 yellow squash, cooked and
   mashed
2 cubes chicken bouillon
3 8-oz. cans of crushed tomatoes
3 cups water (can be adjusted to
   preferred consistency)
Spices (pepper, tarragon, basil,
   oregano)

Yield: 6 servings

Directions

In a large pot, combine all ingredients. Bring to a boil, simmer for one hour until vegetables are tender. Season to taste.

This soup freezes well.

S
O
U
P
S

Cal 89   Fat 3.2 g

Creamy Butternut Squash Soup

You would never think this is low-fat. It's so creamy and rich tasting. The rich orange colour creates a fabulous contrast when served in white bowls.

S O U P S

Ingredients

7 cups butternut squash, peeled, seeded and cubed
4 cups chicken stock
1 ½ cups onion, chopped
½ cup celery, minced very fine (optional)
1 bay leaf

½ tsp. nutmeg
Pinch of ginger
Dash of salt substitute and pepper

1 cup plain low-fat yogurt

Directions

In large saucepan, combine squash, stock, onion, celery and bay leaf. Bring to boil, cover, reduce heat, and simmer until squash is tender, approximately 25 minutes. Remove bay leaf. In blender or food processor, puree soup in batches.

Season with nutmeg, ginger, salt and pepper to taste.

Swirl 2 tablespoons yogurt into each bowl.

Yield: 8 servings

(Soup can be made ahead and frozen for up to 2 months. Thaw and reheat).

Cal 107   Fat 3 g

Yam Soup

Superb!!

Ingredients

3-4 cups water
1 carrot, peeled and sliced
½ zucchini, chopped in bite-
    sized pieces
½ bay leaf

1 leek, chopped thinly
1 yam, cooked

Fresh dill

Directions

Boil carrots and zucchini with bay leaf for 4-5 minutes.

Add leek and carrot for another 2-3 minutes. Peel and dice yam and add to mixture.

A few minutes before serving, add freshly chopped dill.
For a thicker creamy variation, process ½ of yams in blender before adding.

S O U P S

Yield: 4 servings

Cal 73   Fat 2.3 g

Sweet Potato Soup

MICROWAVEABLE

Ingredients

2 medium sweet potatoes, peeled & sliced to ½ inch chunks
2 medium leeks, topped, tailed and chopped
¼ cup chicken stock or water
½ tsp. dillweed

1 ½ cups nonfat milk

4 tsp. parsley (optional)
Low-fat mozzarella cheese (optional)

Yield: 4 servings

Directions

Combine sweet potatoes, leeks, stock and dillweed in a 1 ½ quart dish. Cover with vented plastic wrap and microwave on high until potatoes are just tender, about 4 to 6 minutes. Let stand 4 minutes. For extra creamy soup, process in a blender until smooth.

Meanwhile, pour milk into a 2-cup measuring cup. Microwave on high, uncovered, about 1 ½ - 2 minutes until warm. Whisk milk into the sweet potato mixture and serve warm in heated bowls or mugs.

Sprinkle with parsley and mozzarella cheese if desired.

*Calorie and fat amounts without cheese

Cal 151   Fat 6.2 g

Minestrone Soup

Ingredients

1 10-oz. can chicken bouillon
1 clove garlic, chopped
2 cups onion, chopped
1 cup celery, chopped
4 Tbsp. parsley, finely chopped

9 cups water
1 3-4 oz. can tomato paste
2 carrots, thinly sliced round
1 cup white cabbage, chopped
1 medium whole zucchini, chopped
1 cup fresh or canned red kidney beans
1 tsp. salt
½ tsp. sage
Dash of pepper to taste

1 cup (canned) green beans or peas
1 cup whole wheat elbow macaroni (optional)
Grated parmesan (optional)

Yield: 12 cups

Directions

In large soup pot, stir fry garlic, onion, celery and parsley in 1 tablespoon of broth, cook until tender.

Add remaining broth and water. Stir in tomato paste, carrots, cabbage, zucchini, kidney beans and spices. Mix well, bring to a boil. Reduce heat; cover and simmer slowly for 1 hour.

Add peas and macaroni last. Cook until macaroni is done (7-10 minutes). Sprinkle with grated parmesan if desired.

This recipe submitted by Bonnie Griffith. Calorie and fat amounts without cheese.

SOUPS

Cal 77   Fat 5.5 g

Five-Bean Minestrone

Ingredients

½ cup pinto beans, dried
½ cup white beans, dried
½ cup red kidney beans, dried
½ cup lima beans
9 cups water

½ cup garbanzo beans, canned

1 onion, chopped
1 clove garlic, minced
2 cups chopped celery
¼ cup parsley, chopped
1 tsp. dill

4 cups tomatoes, stewed

2 cups cabbage, shredded
5 cups zucchini, sliced

Yield: 30 servings

Directions

Soak all beans except garbanzos in 9 cups water overnight. Add more water if needed. Change water before cooking beans. Cook beans in 9 cups fresh water for 2-3 hours or until tender.

Add garbanzos and heat thoroughly.

Saute onion, garlic, celery, parsley and dill. Add to cooked beans.

Add tomatoes. Simmer, covered for 45 minutes.

Add cabbage and zucchini, simmering until cooked.

Serve hot. Freezes well.

Cal 99   Fat 0 g

My Famous
Split Pea Soup

Delicious!!

Ingredients

16 oz. dried split green peas
8 cups water
1 stalk celery, chopped
1 medium carrot, chopped
1 small onion, chopped
¾ tsp. thyme
1 bay leaf
Spike or Mrs. Dash to taste

Directions

Place all ingredients in large pot and boil continuously for 20 minutes. Lower heat; simmer until peas are soft, approximately 1 hour.

SOUPS

Yield: 10 servings

Cal 142   Fat 1 g

Lentil Soup

Ingredients

2 cups lentils
4 cups water

1 onion, chopped
2 carrots, chopped
1 potato, diced
2 Morga vegetable cubes
4 Tbsp. dried parsley
Seasonings (garlic, cloves &
    basil)
2 cups canned tomatoes
    (optional)

Directions

In large soup pot add lentils and water. Let simmer until beans are tender.

Add remaining ingredients. Season to taster, and simmer until ingredients are tender.

Serve steaming hot with a slice of whole wheat bread.

Yield: 8 servings

This recipe submitted by Marilyn Mullens

Cal 223   Fat 5.8 g

Hearty Soup with Rice

Ingredients

4 cups water
1 tsp. salt substitute
1 cup sliced carrots
1 cup diced potatoes
3 cups of canned or fresh tomatoes, crushed
1 cup chopped green onion
1 cup canned kidney beans
½ head of cabbage, chopped
   into chunks

½ cup corn, scraped from cob

1 cup cooked brown rice, (keep
   hot)

Directions

In a large pot add all ingredients
except corn and rice. Cover and
simmer for 30 minutes.

Add corn, re-cover and simmer
for 15 minutes.

Serve by spooning some cooked
rice into each bowl; ladle soup
over it.

SOUPS

Yield: 10 servings

Cal 126   Fat 1.1 g

Cabbage Patch Soup

Ingredients

1 Tbsp. margarine
2 medium onions, sliced

8 cups (approx. 1 ½ lbs.) shredded red cabbage
2 potatoes, sliced
1 apple, sliced
8 cups water
1 10½ oz. can condensed beef
  broth
1 tsp. salt substitute
1 small bay leaf
¼ tsp. garlic powder
Dash of sage
Pepper to taste

Yield: 12 servings

Directions

Start preparing soup at least 3 hours prior to serving. In a large pot, sauté onions in margarine until golden.

Add remaining ingredients, and stir. Simmer, covered for 2 hours.

Blend one-sixth of the soup at low speed until creamy. Make sure the lid of container is slightly ajar to allow hot air to escape. Repeat until all the soup is blended.

Cal 70   Fat 0 g

Beans & Barley Soup

This soup has a wonderful texture and taste!

Ingredients

1 large green pepper, chopped
1 medium onion, chopped
1 carrot, chopped
4 cups beef bouillon
½ tsp. prepared mustard
2 Tbsp. minced parsley

1 cup pinto beans, cooked
1 cup small white beans, cooked
¼ cup split peas
¼ cup pearl barley

Directions

Combine green pepper, onion and carrot with beef bouillon, mustard and parsley. Adjust consistency of water, if necessary.

Bring to a boil. Reduce heat, cover, and simmer 45 minutes.

Add beans, peas and barley. Cover and simmer for 1 hour longer until all beans are tender.

Yield: 6 Servings

Cal 166   Fat 0.5 g

Mixed-Bean Gumbo

Ingredients

⅓ cup whole wheat pastry flour
⅔ cup soup stock

3 cups boiling soup stock
1 green pepper, finely chopped
1 stalk celery, finely chopped
1 onion, finely chopped
1 can (14½ oz.) tomatoes,
   chopped
1½ teaspoons minced dried
   mushrooms
2 cloves garlic, minced
2 bay leaves
1 tsp. thyme

2 cups cooked beans*
2 tsp. tabasco sauce or to taste

*Note: Use your choice of
mixed beans; navy, kidney, and
pinto are excellent together.

Yield: 6 servings

Directions

Place the flour in a non-stick fry-ing pan. Cook over medium-high heat, stirring constantly, to roast the flour. Continue stirring until medium brown, about 7 min-utes. Remove from heat and pour in ⅔ cup stock. Whisk until smooth. Transfer flour mixture to a large soup pot.

Add boiling stock, pepper, cel-ery, onion, tomatoes, mushrooms, garlic, bay leaves, and thyme. Bring to a boil, then reduce heat to simmer. Cover loosely and simmer, 15 minutes.

Add beans and tabasco sauce. Continue to simmer until the vegetables are tender, about 15 minutes. Remember to remove bay leaves before serving. Serve hot.

S O U P S

Cal 213   Fat 1 g

Corn Chowder

Ingredients

1 Tbsp. margarine
2 Tbsp. minced onion
2 Tbsp. minced green pepper
½ cup thinly sliced celery

2 Tbsp. flour
1 10½ oz. can condensed light
   cream of chicken soup
2½ cups skimmed milk

Dash of thyme leaves
Dash of tabasco sauce
1 8-oz. can whole kernel corn,
   undrained

Chopped parsley, (optional)

Directions

In medium saucepan sauté onion, green pepper, and celery in margarine until golden.

Stir in flour, followed by soup, then milk. Heat, stirring, to boiling.

Add thyme, tabasco sauce and corn; heat to boiling.

Serve garnished with parsley.

Yield: 5-6 servings

Cal 100   Fat 2.5 g

New Potato Chowder

Ingredients

1 pound new potatoes, cut in ½"
   cubes
3 cups chicken or vegetable
   stock
1 medium leek, topped, tailed
   and chopped, tough outer
   green leaves removed
1 tsp. marjoram
4 cloves garlic, peeled and thinly sliced

¼ cup minced fresh chives
½ cup evaporated skim milk

Directions

Combine potatoes, stock, leek, marjoram and garlic in a large saucepan and bring to a boil. Reduce heat to medium-low, cover loosely and simmer until the potatoes are tender, about 15 minutes.

Stir in chives and milk and continue to simmer just until heated through. Serve soup warm.

Yield: 4–6 servings

Cal 127   Fat 1 g

Old-Style
Chunky Chicken Soup

Ingredients

1 5-lb. stewing chicken (skin removed)
8 cups water
½ tsp. salt substitute

8-10 medium sized potatoes, peeled and cubed
2 16-oz. cans tomatoes (low-sodium), crushed
1 tsp. dried parsley flakes
1 tsp. dried basil, oregano and sage

2 16-oz. cans whole kernel corn, drained
1 16-oz. can lima beans, drained.

Yield: 15 servings

Directions

Combine chicken, water and salt in Dutch oven. Bring to a boil; reduce heat. Cover, let simmer for 1 hour or until tender. Remove chicken and while cooling, strain stock through a large colander. Skim off any fat. After chicken is cool enough, remove meat and cut into bite-sized pieces.

Combine potatoes, undrained tomatoes, and spices in strained stock. Bring to a boil, reduce heat. Cover and let simmer for 20 minutes or until potatoes are tender.

Add chicken, corn and lima beans and let simmer 20 minutes or more. Season to taste.

Cal 199   Fat 3 g

Chicken Cheddar Soup

A thrifty, wholesome meal!

S
O
U
P
S

Ingredients

1 Tbsp. margarine
1 ½ cups each chopped onion,
  celery, and carrot

2 Tbsp. flour
3 cups water
3 packets instant chicken broth
  and seasoning mix

1 ½ cups fresh or frozen asparagus cuts or tips

1 ½ cups skim milk
4 ounces low-fat Cheddar
  cheese, shredded

10 –12 ounces skinned and
  boned cooked chicken, diced
3 cups cooked small whole
  wheat macaroni (i.e., shells,
  elbows, tubetti, etc.)
1 Tbsp. Worcestershire sauce
Dash of pepper

Yield: 6 servings

Directions

In large pot heat margarine over
medium heat until bubbly and
hot. Saute onion, celery, and
carrot until tender.

Sprinkle vegetables with flour
and combine, stirring quickly.
Gradually stir in water.
Add broth mix and bring to a
boil, stirring constantly.

Add asparagus and cook, stirring, about 4 minutes.

Add milk and cheese and continue stirring. Cook until cheese
has melted. Reduce heat to low.

Add remaining ingredients, and
continue cooking until heated
thoroughly.

Cal 371   Fat 6.8 g

Speedy Gazpacho

Ingredients

1 medium cucumber, pared

½ cup finely chopped celery
½ cup finely chopped green pepper
5 cups chilled tomato juice
1 Tbsp. olive oil
1 tsp. chopped parsley
½ tsp. oregano leaves
Dash of tabasco sauce
Dash of Worcestershire sauce

12 ice cubes

Directions

About 10 minutes before serving, cut 6 thin slices from pared cucumber. Dice remaining.

At high speed, blend cucumber and all remaining ingredients, except ice cubes until smooth.

In chilled bowls, pour soup over ice cubes. Garnish with cucumber slices.

**S
O
U
P
S**

Yield: 6 servings

Cal 70   Fat 2.2 g

Tooty-Fruity Soup

Ingredients

1 pint strawberries, sliced
1 lb. rhubarb, chopped
1 ¼ cups pineapple juice

approx. ½ cup artificial sweetener

¼ cup chopped orange segments

Directions

Start preparing 3 hours before serving. In medium pan, combine strawberry slices (reserve some for garnish), rhubarb and juice. Simmer for 10 minutes.

Stir in sugar sweetener to taste; cool. In covered blender container, blend fruit mixture one-half at a time.

Fold in orange segments. Cover and refrigerate.

Serve soup garnished with reserved strawberry slices.

Yield: 6 servings

Cal 115   Fat "tr"

Festive Tomato Soup

This is great hot or cold!

Ingredients

- 1 6-oz. can frozen orange juice concentrate
- 3 juice cans water
- 2 10¾ oz. cans low-cal condensed tomato soup

Directions

Start to prepare 15 minutes prior to serving.

In large saucepan, heat all the ingredients to a gentle simmer.

Serve.

SOUPS

Yield: 6 servings

Cal 44

Fat "tr"

Italian Tomato Sauce

Ingredients

cooking spray
1 or 2 cloves minced garlic

4 cups tomatoes, crushed

1 6-oz. can tomato paste
1 bay leaf
2 tsp. salt
½ tsp. oregano
½ tsp. basil

1 tsp. sugar (optional) or grated carrot if tomatoes are too bitter.

Yield:

Directions

Saute garlic in pan coated with cooking spray.

Strain or puree tomatoes in blender and add to oil and garlic.

Add remaining ingredients to sauce and simmer until thick.

Variations:

Spanish Style
Use above recipe, adding 1 cup chopped onions and ½ cup diced green pepper.

Mexican Style
Use Spanish variation, adding 1 tsp. cumin to the sauce.

Chunky Style
Use Spanish variation, adding sliced celery and mushrooms.

Cal 147   Fat "tr"

Spaghetti Sauce

This is fantastic sauce!

Ingredients

½ cup onion, chopped
½ cup celery, chopped
½ cup carrot, finely chopped
1 clove garlic, minced
cooking spray

1 28 oz. can tomatoes, cut up
¼ cup dry red wine
1 bay leaf
2 Tbsp. snipped parsley
1 tsp. chicken bouillon
1 tsp. marjoram
½ tsp. sugar
⅛ tsp. pepper

1 3-lb. spaghetti squash
(optional)

Yield: 6 servings

Directions

In large saucepan cook onion, celery, carrot and garlic in cooking oil till tender but not brown.

Add tomatoes, wine, bay leaf, parsley, bouillon granules, marjoram, sugar and pepper. Bring to a boil, reduce heat. Boil gently, uncovered, about 45 minutes or till desired consistency, stirring occasionally. Discard bay leaf.

Meanwhile, quarter squash; remove seeds and strings. Place in microwave baking dish with enough water to cover bottom of dish. Cover with wax paper. Cook on high in microwave for 15 minutes, or until tender, rotating dish halfway through cooking time.

This recipe was submitted by Lorie Grant

SOUPS

Cal 135

Fat "tr"

Low-Fat Gravy

Ingredients

2 Tbsp. cornstarch
2 cups beef or turkey bouillon
Dash of pepper and salt substitute

Directions

Whisk cornstarch into cool bouillon.

Heat, stirring constantly, until mixture thickens.

Season to taste

Yield: 4 servings

Cal 17

Fat "tr"

Low-Cal Tartar Sauce

Ingredients

1 cup light mayonnaise
1 Tbsp. minced dill pickle
1 Tbsp. lemon juice
1 tsp. grated onion
1 tsp. minced parsley
1 tsp. chopped pimiento

Directions

Combine ingredients. Serve chilled. Refrigerate unused portions.

SOUPS

Yield: 10 oz.

Calorie and fat measurements per ounce

Cal 5.4   Fat 1 g

Tofu Sauce for Chicken Seafood or Vegetables

Ingredients

8 oz. tofu, pressed
2 Tbsp. plus 2 tsp. water
2 Tbsp. plus 2 tsp. lemon juice
Season to taste

Directions

Blend ingredients until smooth.

Yield: 4 servings

Calories and fat per ounce

Cal 22

Fat 2 g

Hot & Spicy Cheese Dip

Ingredients

1 medium onion, chopped (½ cup)
2 cloves garlic, minced
2 tsp. margarine or vegetable oil

3 large tomatoes, peeled, seeded, and chopped
1 4-oz. can green chili peppers, rinsed, seeded and chopped
½ tsp. chili powder
¼ tsp. tabasco sauce

1 Tbsp. cornstarch
1 Tbsp. cold water

½ cup shredded low-fat cheddar cheese (2 ounces)
8 7-inch flour tortillas, cut into wedges

Yield: 16 servings

Directions

In a medium saucepan tenderize onion and garlic in hot oil but do not brown.

Stir in tomatoes, chili peppers, chili powder, and tabasco sauce. Boil gently, uncovered, over medium heat for 10 minutes, stirring occasionally.

Combine cornstarch and water and stir into tomato mixture. Cook and stir till thick and bubbly. Cook and stir for 2 minutes more.

Stir in cheese till melted. Serve dip warm with tortilla wedges.

Calorie and fat measurements per 2 tablespoons:

S O U P S

Cal 62   Fat 2 g

White-Bean Dip

*Satisfying for those cravings for
something creamy!*

S
O
U
P
S

Ingredients

1 can (15½ oz.) cannellini beans,
    drained and rinsed
1 Tbsp. fresh lemon juice
2 Tbsp. plain low-fat yogurt
1 Tbsp. chopped fresh parsley
¼ tsp. tabasco sauce
Dash of salt and pepper

1 tsp. minced garlic

Directions

Combine all ingredients, except
garlic in food processor. Process
until smooth, then transfer to
small bowl.

Stir in garlic. Season to taste.
Serve with toasted pita triangles
or cut-up vegetables.

Yield: 1 ¼ cups

*Calorie and fat measurements
per tablespoon:*

Cal 20

Fat 1 g

Low-Cal Sour Cream Dip

Serve with oven-fried potato chips or tortilla chips.

Ingredients

1 ¾ cups light sour cream
1 ½ tsp. dried dillweed
1 ½ tsp. minced green onion
1 ½ tsp. snipped parsley

Directions

In small bowl stir together Low-Cal Sour Cream, dillweed, green onion and parsley. Cover and chill.

SOUPS

Yield: 1 ¾ cups

Calorie and fat measurements per tablespoon:

Cal 25

Fat 1 g

Veggie Dip

Ingredients

1 cup plain low-fat yogurt
⅓ cup light mayonnaise
1 Tbsp. minced onion
1 tsp. dillweed
1 Tbsp. chopped parsley
1 tsp. seasoning salt
1 tsp. dry mustard
2 slices crisp crumbled cooked
   bacon (optional)

Directions

Combine all ingredients, mix thoroughly. Keep refrigerated until serving.

Serve with carrot sticks, celery sticks, cherry tomatoes, radishes, zucchini, cucumber sticks, green peppers, and cauliflowerettes.

This recipe was submitted by Marilyn Mullens.

Calorie and fat measurements per ounce.

Yield: 1¼ cups

Cal 48.2   Fat 3 g

Cheese Spread

Try this creamy sensation with assorted vegetables and whole wheat crackers!

Ingredients

¾ cup finely shredded carrot*
2 Tbsp. finely chopped onion
2 Tbsp. snipped parsley
1 Tbsp. grated parmesan cheese (optional)
½ tsp. curry powder

1 8-oz. package light cream cheese, softened

½ cup snipped alfalfa sprouts
* reserve ¼ cup shredded carrot for garnish

Directions

In a small mixing bowl stir together ½ cup carrot, onion, parsley, parmesan cheese, and curry powder.

Add the cream cheese. Combine well. Transfer to a serving bowl.

Sprinkle with alfalfa sprouts and the remaining ¼ cup carrot. Cover and chill to store. Serve with small knives to spread on vegetables.

Yield: 1⅓ cups

Calorie and fat measurements per tablespoon.

Cal 12   Fat 3 g

The Best of Beans and More!

Beans

THE FAT BURNERS

BEANS are a dieter's Best Friend. They are naturally low in calories and filling. Beans have the most protein with the least fat of any food, high in potassium but low in sodium. Combining beans with a whole grain such as rice, barley, wheat, etc. rounds out the complement of amino acids that form the protein. Best known for their ability to bind water in the gastrointestinal tract and increase fecal bulk which helps fight constipation. The real benefits of beans are too numerous to mention. They can lower cholesterol, control diabetes and they definitely increase feelings of fullness also. Since fibre tolerance varies from individual to individual, and too quick a boost can lead to stomach cramps, bloating or flatulence, **Slowly** increase your intake each day. Also drink at least 8 glasses of water daily. Meals rich in fibre like beans could reduce the calorie total by approximately 5%. There have been studies in which overweight people have lost inches by only adding fibre and water to their diet. So what are you waiting for? Let's find out how to prepare this excellent **fat burner**.

Before cooking, rinse the beans and remove foreign particles. The next step is to soak them, it's not necessary if you plan to cook them all day but soaking them removes some of the water soluble chemical compounds which cause flatulence or gas. Beans will double in size as a result of soaking, and it also shortens the cooking time.

Cover the cleaned beans with water and allow them to soak overnight, or for 8-10 hours at room temperature. Use 6-8 cups of water for 2 cups dry beans. Discard the water after soaking. The reason for this is it lessens the discomforts of gas by not using the leftover water to prepare your dish, although there is some loss of nutrients.

STOVE-TOP METHOD: Use heavy metal pots, stainless steel or cast iron. The pot must have a tight fitting lid. Cover soaked beans with water, bring to a boil, cover and reduce heat. Simmer until beans are tender, 30 minutes to 3 hours, depending on the type of bean.

CROCK POT METHOD: You need to experiment with times and settings, it can be tricky. Try cooking soaked beans on High for 2 to 3 hours - then cook on Low for 6 to 8 hours. During cooking on High check to make sure the beans are continually covered with water.

MICROWAVE OVENS: They are not satisfactory for cooking beans but they are wonderful for thawing frozen cooked beans, casseroles or reheating bean dishes.

OVEN METHOD: This method is used in combination with other methods to make baked beans. Be sure to use cooked beans which are not over-cooked. Use glass, ceramic or earthenware not metal baking pans. Combine ingredients, cover and bake for 1 to 1½ hours at 300°. To brown beans, remove the cover and bake 15 to 30 minutes longer.

Pick the method you find convenient, simply cook the beans until they are tender. **Do not overcook!**

BEANS (1 CUP DRIED)	CUPS OF WATER	COOKING TIME
SOYBEANS	4	3-4 HOURS
CHICK PEAS (GARBANZO BEANS)	3	3 HOURS
PINTO AND KIDNEY BEANS	3	3 HOURS
LENTILS	3	1 HOUR
SPLIT PEAS	3	1 HOUR

TIP: High acid foods such as tomatoes, tend to slow the cooking time. If you need to add vinegar or tomatoes, be sure to add them near the end of the cooking time.

Cooked beans store well. They keep well in an airtight container in the fridge for at least 5 days. In fact, bean soups and casseroles always taste better the second day because the flavours continue to blend. Beans also freeze well. Thaw beans slowly in the fridge overnight or at room temperature, then simmer until warm.

Chinese Casserole

This dish is economical and makes a great presentation.

Ingredients

1 cup soybean sprouts
½ cup green beans
1 medium onion, chopped (to make 1 cup)
1 8-oz. can sliced mushrooms (reserve liquid)*
1 cup celery, chopped
2 Tbsp. oil
½ cup canned (Chinese) noodles
1 cup liquid from mushrooms* (add liquid from chestnuts if not enough)
2 tsp. salt substitute
Dash of pepper

1 cup fine dry egg noodles
1 cup sliced water chestnuts

Directions

Combine all ingredients except egg noodles and chestnuts. Layer top with last ingredients. Bake for 1 hour at 350°.

B E A N S

Yield: 6 servings

Cal 159   Fat 4 g

Mediterranean Casserole

Ingredients

4 cups chick peas, cooked
¼ cup water or vegetable broth
1 can light mushroom soup
3 Tbsp. parsley, chopped
Other seasonings as desired
   (e.g. oregano)
1 tsp. low-sodium soy sauce

Directions

Combine all ingredients. Bake covered at 350° for 45 minutes.

**B
E
A
N
S**

Yield: 6 servings

Cal 250   Fat 5 g

Cheese and Pimiento Loaf

Ingredients

3 pimientos, chopped
½ lb. light cream cheese
2 egg whites
2 cups white lima beans, cooked
   & mashed
4 Tbsp. onion, chopped
2 Tbsp. parsley, chopped
¾ cup pumpernickel or rye
   bread crumbs
Dash of salt substitute

Directions

Combine ingredients and shape into a loaf. Sprinkle with additional crumbs. Bake in a 325° oven for one hour.

B E A N S

Yield: 6 servings

Cal 288   Fat 4 g

Chick Pea Loaf

Ingredients

1 cup chick peas, cooked &
  mashed
1 onion, chopped
¼ cup chopped green peppers,
  or celery or mushrooms
  (optional)
1 whole egg
2 egg whites
½ cup low sodium tomato soup
  or 1% milk
1 tsp. Spike or Mrs. Dash

Directions

Combine all ingredients. Bake in
a 350° oven for 45 minutes.

**B
E
A
N
S**

Yield: 4 servings

Cal 150   Fat 3 g

Carrot-Bean Loaf

Ingredients

4 cups cooked soybeans,
   mashed
2 cups carrots, shredded
1 onion, chopped
½ cup celery, chopped
1 cup dried 100% whole wheat
   crumbs
1 cup wheat germ
2 tsp. Spike or Mrs. Dash
1 Tbsp. butter substitute
   (optional)

Directions

Mix all ingredients thoroughly.
Pack into a well greased pan.
Bake at 350° about 45 min-
utes.

BEANS

Yield: 8 servings

Cal 272   Fat 7.7 g

Garbanzo/Vegetable Sandwich Filling

Great in Pita Bread

Ingredients

1 1-lb. can garbanzos (mashed with fork)
¼ tsp. garlic powder
¼ tsp. cumin
2 tsp. parsley, chopped
1 Tbsp. lemon juice
Dash of salt & pepper

Cucumber, chopped
Tomatoes, chopped
Onion, chopped
1 cup plain low-fat yogurt

Wholewheat bread or pitas
Shredded lettuce

Directions

Combine beans, spices, and lemon juice. Refrigerate for at least one hour.

Combine chopped vegetables and yogurt. Chill.

Spread bread or fill pitas with garbanzo mixture. Spoon on vegetable combination. Top with lettuce.

Variation

Mix yogurt with onion soup mix. Try with assorted vegetables i.e. radishes, mushrooms, green pepper or alfalfa sprouts.

BEANS

Yield: 6 servings

Cal 166   Fat 2 g

Lentil Bean Patties

Very quick and tasty!

Ingredients

1 small onion, chopped

2 cups lentils, cooked and
    mashed
¾ tsp. Spike or Mrs. Dash

Optional: ½ cup chopped
    walnuts

Directions

Sauté onion in pan sprayed with vegetable oil.

Combine all ingredients. Form into patties. Place on non-stick sheet and brown in oven. Serve with low-sodium tomato sauce.

**B
E
A
N
S**

Yield: 4 servings

Calories and fat without nuts

Cal 216   Fat "tr"

Soy Cutlets

Ingredients

½ cup dry soybeans

1 cup water

½ cup corn meal
1 cup oatmeal, dry
1 medium onion, chopped
½ cup celery, chopped
½ tsp. Spike or Mrs. Dash
3 Tbsp. low-sodium soy sauce

Directions

Immerse soy beans in water and soak overnight.

Combine drained soy beans with 1 cup water and mix in blender until finely ground.

Add remaining ingredients and mix well. Let stand about 10 minutes to absorb moisture. Drop by tablespoons on non-stick skillet. Brown lightly on both sides. Place in baking dish. Bake at 350° for 20 minutes. Cover with low-sodium tomato sauce or low-fat gravy (See *Sauces* in chapter *Soups On!*).

Bake until heated thoroughly.

Yield: 6 servings

BEANS

Cal 173   Fat 4.5 g

Meatless Stew

Ingredients

2 Tbsp. olive oil
1 cup onions, sliced
½ cup green peppers, sliced

2 cups whole corn kernels
2 cups cooked black beans or 1
  cup each of lima beans and
  navy beans

⅓ cup tomatoes (fresh or
  canned)
2 cups sliced zucchini
½ cup celery & carrot, finely
  chopped
Dash of salt substitute
¼ cup parsley, chopped
1 tsp. basil

Directions

Sauté vegetables in oil.

Add corn and beans. Cook on
low heat for 15 minutes.

Add remaining ingredients and
cook on low heat, 20-30 minutes or until vegetables are
tender.

B E A N S

Yield: 8 servings

Cal 158   Fat 6 g

Bean Tortillas

Ingredients

1 cup dry pinto beans

1 10-oz. can low-sodium tomato
   soup
1 tsp. onion salt

12 tortillas, whole wheat
Shredded lettuce
Chopped onions and tomatoes
   as desired

Optional: Sprinkle lightly with
   low-fat shredded cheese.

Directions

Soak beans overnight and then
cook until tender. Drain.

Add soup and onion salt to
beans and heat thoroughly.

Fold tortillas in half. Fill partially
with bean mixture. Top with lettuce, onions and tomatoes.
Also great with low-fat shredded
cheese.

BEANS

Yield: 12 tortillas

Cal 163   Fat 1 g

Soybean Soufflé

Ingredients

1 cup dry soybeans

2 Tbsp. canola oil
2 tsp. poultry seasoning
¼ tsp. basil
2 tsp. salt substitute

Directions

Soak beans overnight. Add approximately 2 cups water and liquefy in blender. This should make 5 cups pulp mixture.

Add remaining ingredients and mix well. Pour into a shallow pan so that soufflé is not more than two inches thick. Bake at 300° for 1½ - 2 hours. Soufflé puffs up, but as it cools it will shrink. Serve with Low-Cal Tartar Sauce. (See *Sauces* in chapter: *Soups On!*).

**B
E
A
N
S**

Yield: 6 servings

Cal 176   Fat 6 g

Potato-Nut Patties

Ingredients

1 cup boiling water
½ cup oatmeal, dry

½ cup ground buckwheat groats
1 cup mashed potatoes
½ tsp. salt substitute
1 Tbsp. brewer's yeast

¼ cup high fibre cereal crumbs
   or corn flakes crumbs
½ cup 100% whole wheat flour

Directions

Stir oats into boiling water and cook until thick.

Combine nuts, potatoes, salt and yeast together. Add cooked oatmeal and mix. Form into patties.

Mix crumbs and flour for breading. Dip patties into mixture and fry in a non-stick pan until golden brown.

Yield: 4 servings

Cal 346   Fat 2.2 g

Great Northern Beans

Ingredients

3 cups dried Great Northern
   beans
8 cups water

½ cup green beans
1 large white onion or leek,
   diced
1 large green or red pepper,
   diced
1 cup stewed or whole fresh
   tomatoes, crushed
1 bay leaf
1 clove garlic, chopped fine
1 tsp. mint
1 tsp. paprika

2 Tbsp. olive oil

Yield: 6-8 servings

Directions

Wash beans carefully and look
for stones. Soak for 24 hours.
Rinse. Place in a pot with the
water, and bring to a boil.
Reduce heat and simmer for
approximately 45 minutes.

Add remaining ingredients
(except oil), and cook vegetables
until tender (approximately 10
minutes).

Take 1 cup of the mixture, place
in a blender with the olive oil
and blend until smooth. Return
to the pot to thicken. Garnish
with fresh mint. Serve with salad
and steamed swiss chard if
desired.

**B
E
A
N
S**

Cal 350   Fat 5 g

Mom's Baked Beans

MEATLESS

Ingredients

3 cups red kidney beans (or
   mixture)
2½ cups canned tomatoes
¾ cup brown sugar (do not omit)
½ cup molasses
12 mushrooms, sliced
1 medium onion, chopped
1 green pepper, chopped
1 zucchini, chopped (optional)
2 tsp. dry mustard
Pepper and salt to taste

Directions

Soak enough beans overnight to
make 3 cups. Combine all the
ingredients in a crockpot, bean-
pot or suitable dish with cover
for oven. (If too dry during cooking; add more tomatoes or
tomato juice). Bake in oven at
300° or slow cook for 12½-
13 hours.

Yield: 8 8-oz. servings

*This recipe submitted by Valerie
Morris.*

Cal 204

Fat "tr"

CHAPTER 4

Secrets of Tasty Tofu Recipes

1. Tofu French Toast
2. Emilie's Tofu Breakfast Treat
3. Thousand Island Dressing
4. Creamy Onion Dressing
5. Tahini Tofu Dressing or Dip
6. Mild Curry Dressing or Dip
7. Creamy Tofu Spread
8. Tofu Mock Egg Salad
9. Spinach Tofu Dip
10. Egg Foo Yong
11. Arrowroot Sauce
12. Lasagna
13. Stir-Fried Vegetables with Tofu
14. Curried Grains and Vegetables
15. Mild Curry Sauce
16. Tofu Stuffed Zucchini
17. Vegetable & Tofu Shish Kebabs
18. Rice Salad Roll-ups with Tofu and Tahini Sauce
19. Tofu Cutlets (Variations: Curried/Herb)
20. Carob Mint Tofu Pudding
21. Almond Carob Tofu Pudding
22. Easy Tofu Fruit Parfaits (Variations: Strawberry/ Blueberry/Pineapple-Coconut)
23. Tofu Cheesecake
24. Carob Tofu Cheesecake
25. Strawberry Topping for Tofu Cheesecake
26. Tofu Fruit Smoothie
27. Tofu Whipped Cream

The following chapter of wonderful tofu recipes has been donated graciously by Jeanne Marie Martin. She has included tofu treats from "breakfasts" to tofu whipped "cream."

Jeanne Marie, is a Natural Food Consultant with 20 years of experience in the health field, which is highlighted by 19 years of teaching cooking classes and over 15 years of business and private diet consulting.

Jeanne Marie has traveled extensively throughout North America collecting recipes, menus and information for her work. She has cooked for three Natural Food Restaurants and owned her own catering business for three years, besides managing a health food store in Thunder Bay and more recently one in Vancouver.

She is author of over 100 articles for more than a dozen magazines in Canada and the U.S. Dozens of Canadian and U.S. Medical Doctors, Naturopathic Physicians and Chiropractors recommend her books, classes and consultations.

Thousands of students can attest to the fact that she makes natural foods attractive, delicious and easy-to-prepare. This chapter, based specifically on tofu, will open up a whole new world of cooking for you.

I am pleased to be able to include these tasty recipes for a calcium-rich protein alternative, which sometimes requires different methods to prepare.

Jeanne Marie's expertise in this field was invaluable. I greatly appreciate her contribution as an enhancement to the *201 Fat-Burning Recipes* cookbook.

Tofu French Toast

Ingredients

7-8 oz. (½ lb.) tofu, crumbled
¾ cup milk, soy or nut milk or
  water
1-2 Tbsp. oil
3-4 tsp. liquid sweetener
1 tsp. vanilla extract
½ tsp. cinnamon
Several dashes sea salt

Extras:
Bread
Fruit, sliced, blended or stewed
Maple syrup or other liquid
sweetener

Directions

Blend all the main ingredients
(not extras) in a blender or food
processor. Heat a well-oiled frying pan on medium-high heat.
Dip the bread in the mixture
and place several pieces in the
hot pan. Cook a few minutes on
each side until lightly browned
and serve with maple syrup
and/or fruit or jam. (Re-oil the
pan before cooking each batch).

Yield: 10 slices

T
O
F
U

Emilie's Tofu Breakfast Treat

Enjoy this very different, delicious breakfast as a nice change. Make just enough, fresh for each day.

Ingredients

3-4 slices regular tofu, ¼-⅓ inch thick
3 Tbsp. nutritional yeast
1 Tbsp. olive oil or other oil
1 tsp. tamari soy sauce
¼-⅓ tsp. onion powder
Several dashes cayenne red pepper and sea kelp

Directions

Mix all the ingredients except the tofu together thoroughly. Put the tofu pieces in an unoiled small iron skillet or tin pan and spread the paste on top of each tofu piece like jam. Bake in a pre-heated oven at 350° for 15-20 minutes or until tender and juicy.

TOFU

Yield: 1 serving

Thousand Islands Dressing

Ingredients

6 oz. tofu, crumbled
¼ cup nut milk or slightly more
2-3 Tbsp. each ketchup and
   apple cider vinegar
1-2 tsp. tamari soy sauce
1-2 tsp. onion, finely minced
Cayenne red pepper and sea
   salt to taste
3-4 Tbsp. pickle relish or
   chopped pickles

Directions

Blend or use a food processor for all ingredients except the pickles. Stir in the pickles last. Add a bit of liquid sweetener if desired. Chill and serve. Keeps up to 7 days or so.

Yield: 12 oz.

T
O
F
U

Creamy Onion Dressing

Ingredients

6 oz. tofu, crumbled
⅓ - ½ cup nut or soy milk or
   slightly more
3-6 green onions, chopped fine
   (add some after processing)
2 tsp. tamari soy sauce
1-2 tsp. parsley
½ tsp. each basil and paprika
Sea salt or vegetized sea salt to
   taste
Several dashes cayenne red
   pepper

Directions

Blend or food process all ingredients well and chill before
serving. Add a bit of sweetening
if desired. Keeps 4-7 days.

T O F U

Yield: 10 –12 oz.

Tahini Tofu
Dressing or Dip

Though this recipe is nutritionally very rich, it is also higher in fat. Suggest you have for a noon meal

Ingredients

6 oz. tofu, crumbled
½ cup sesame tahini
½ cup oil
½ - ⅔ cup lemon juice, fresh squeezed
¼ cup water
2 Tbsp. fresh parsley, chopped or 1 Tbsp. dried parsley
2-4 tsp. tamari soy sauce or dark miso
4-6 green onion tops only, chopped
2-3 cloves garlic, minced
½ tsp. each: paprika and sea salt
⅛ tsp. sea kelp
Cayenne red pepper to taste

Directions

Blend or use a food processor for all ingredients except 2-3 of the green onion tops. Chop the remaining green onions small and add to the mixture for texture. Chill and serve. Keeps 3-5 days refrigerated. For a vegetable or cracker dip for parties, decrease the oil ¼ cup and add ¼ cup extra water to the recipe.

Yield: 3 cups (24 oz.)

TOFU

Mild Curry Dressing or Dip

Ingredients

7-8 oz. tofu
1 cup nut or soy milk
2-3 tsp. honey or other liquid
sweetener
1-1½ tsp. curry powder
½ tsp. turmeric
¼ tsp. each: paprika, cumin and
chili powder
⅛ tsp. ginger
Sea salt or vegetized sea salt to
taste
Cayenne red pepper to taste

Directions

Blend or use a food processor to mix all ingredients thoroughly. Chill one hour before using as a dressing or vegetable dip. Keeps 4-8 days refrigerated.

Yield: 16 oz.

TOFU

Creamy Tofu Spread

Use this tasty, high protein spread to stuff tomatoes, green peppers or celery. It also makes a great sandwich or cracker spread.

Ingredients

8 oz. tofu, crumbled
⅓ cup sesame tahini
4-5 tsp. tamari soy sauce or dark miso
2 Tbsp. onion, finely minced
1 clove garlic, finely minced or crushed
1 scant tsp. apple cider vinegar
¼ tsp. sea kelp

Optional: 1/2 cup green onion tops, chives or nuts, finely chopped

Optional: 1 tsp. of one of the following: caraway seeds, dill weed or cumin seeds

Yield: 14 oz.

Directions

Mix everything together in a food processor or homogenizing juicer except for the optional items that should be stirred in last. About ½ cup of finely chopped celery or green pepper, may also be added if desired. Keeps 3-7 days refrigerated depending on how many fresh vegetables are included.

TOFU

Tofu Mock Egg Salad

Ingredients

12-14 oz. tofu, crumbled
2 stalks celery or ½ green pepper, very finely chopped
1 small tomato, seeded, chopped very finely and paper towel dried
1 bunch green onions, just the tops, chopped finely
½ tsp. garlic powder
¼ tsp. paprika
Several dashes each: cayenne red pepper and sea kelp
Vegetable sea salt to taste

Optional: Several dashes turmeric for a yellow colouring

Optional: ¼ tsp. celery seed and/or 1-2 tsp. parsley

Directions

Mix all the ingredients together well and serve with crackers or in pita bread/flatbreads. It can also be stuffed in a tomato, bell pepper or in celery. It keeps 2-4 days refrigerated.

Yield: 16 oz.

T
O
F
U

Spinach Tofu Dip

Ingredients

1 lb. spinach (2 cups firmly
   packed)

6-8 oz. tofu, crumbled

2-3 tsp. parsley
½ tsp. basil
⅛ tsp. each: marjoram, oregano,
   thyme, paprika
Several dashes each: cayenne
   red pepper and sea kelp
Vegetable sea salt and/or tamari
   soy sauce to taste

Directions

Swish the spinach leaves in
water to remove all the sand.
Rinse and then steam the
spinach leaves 8-12 minutes
until tender.

Wash the tofu and dry off any
excess water.

Use a food processor to liquefy
all ingredients. Correct seasonings according to your own
taste. If a food processor is
unavailable, use a blender and a
few drops of water if needed.
Blend, stop the machine and stir
and blend again. Repeat the
process until blended smooth.

TOFU

Yield: 2 servings

Egg Foo Yong

A tasty meal or snack.

Ingredients

6 eggs, beaten until foamy
2-3 tsp. light oil
1 Tbsp. tamari soy sauce
⅛ - ¼ tsp. sea salt
⅛ tsp. paprika

6-8 oz. regular tofu, mashed
3-4 oz. mung bean sprouts
6-10 mushrooms, chopped or
     sliced
¼ cup green onion tops
Optional: 2-4 oz. shredded crab
     or baby shrimp

Extra oil for sautéing

**Yield: 3–5 servings,
        makes 12 patties**

Directions

Beat all the liquid ingredients
and herbs together well.

Then mix in the mashed tofu,
vegetables and seafood if
desired.

Moderately oil a large skillet or
griddle and heat until fairly hot.
Drop about 3-4 tablespoons (¼
cup or less) of the mixture onto
one side of the skillet. Make 2-3
more as room permits. Fry until
the bottoms are browned, about
1-3 minutes on medium heat.
Turn over with a spatula (turner)
for about 1 minute more or until
cooked through but still tender.
Re-oil the skillet for each batch.
Serve hot immediately or keep
in a warmed oven until serving.

CONTINUED NEXT PAGE

TOFU

Make sure to stir the mixture well before making each patty, which should be about as big as a large pancake. Serve covered with Arrowroot Sauce or tamari soy sauce. Keeps 3-5 days refrigerated. Re-heat in the oven.

TOFU

Arrowroot Sauce

D E L I C I O U S   S A U C E

Ingredients

1 ½ cups water
5 tsp. arrowroot powder

2-3 Tbsp. tamari soy sauce
1-2 vegetable bouillon cubes or
   1-2 tsp. vegetable broth powder
Several dashes each: cayenne
   red pepper and sea kelp

Directions

Mix the arrowroot thoroughly
with the water in a saucepan
with a wire whisk.

Then add the remaining ingredients and mix well. Cook over a
medium heat, stirring constantly, until thickened. Keep warm
over low heat. Keeps refrigerated up to 7 days or may be
frozen.

T
O
F
U

Yield: 16–18 oz.

Lasagna

The tofu adds protein, nutrients and flavour to the dish. It absorbs the sauce, takes on its flavour and tastes wonderful.

Ingredients

4-5 cups tomato sauce
8-12 lasagna noodles, cooked and cooled

12 oz. cottage cheese or ricotta

6-8 oz. tofu, mashed
1-1½ lbs. mozzarella cheese, grated

Optional: 1-2 cups mushrooms, eggplant or zucchini, sliced small

Optional: ¼ lb. extra cheddar or swiss cheese, grated

Yield: 6–8 servings

Directions

Lightly oil the lasagna pan (9" x 13"). Spread 1-2 cups sauce on the bottom of the pan, just enough to lightly cover the bottom. Then add a single layer of noodles. Broken and small noodle pieces can also be used.

Next, spread out all the cottage cheese or ricotta and on top of this add half of the remaining sauce. If vegetables are used, add these as the next layer.

The second and last layer of noodles comes next followed by the tofu. Next, the last layer of sauce is added. Then add all the remaining grated cheese. Spread the layers evenly. Bake at 350° for 35-50 minutes until cooked through. Be sure not to overcook the top layer of cheese, especially when reheating, or it will harden, use a tent of loose tin foil to cover it for a short time if necessary. Keeps 4-7 days and may be frozen.

TOFU

Stir-Fried Vegetables with Tofu

Ingredients

Yield: 4 servings

2-3 Tbsp. toasted sesame oil or other

2-3 large carrots, sliced on a long slant - ⅛ inch thick

1 small piece of ginger, cut in very thin slices

½ head or less Chinese cabbage or regular green cabbage

4 stalks celery or bok choy, sliced on a slant - ¼ inch thick

3-4 green onions, chopped in small, slanted pieces

2-4 cloves garlic, sliced in 3-4 pieces each – lengthwise

1 green pepper or 1 stalk celery, chopped in long, thin pieces

1 cup mushrooms, sliced ¼ inch thick (from cap to stem)

1 cup mung bean sprouts

⅛ - ¼ cup tamari soy sauce

Optional: ½ cup of broccoli flowerets, edible pea pods and/or sliced water chestnuts

Directions

Heat the oil in a wok or big iron skillet on medium-high heat. When the oil is hot, add the hardest vegetables first: carrots, ginger, and broccoli, if any and stir almost constantly.

After these cook for a few minutes, add the cabbage, celery, onions, garlic and peppers, if any. Stir these a few more minutes until everything is nearly as tender as desired.

At the last minute add the remaining mushrooms, mung sprouts and pea pods or water chestnuts, if any.

Just before serving, pour on the tamari soy sauce. Serve hot over whole grains if possible. Enjoy immediately as this dish does not store well.

Curried Grains and Vegetables

This delightfully mild, yet flavourful dish is a special treat. A work of art for festive occasions and company.

Yield: 4 servings

Ingredients

1 cup whole dry grain, cooked and hot (makes 2 to 2 ½ cups) Use brown rice, millet, kasha, quinoa or other grain

1 cup tofu chunks – tofu from RICE ROLL-UPS, TOFU CUT-LETS or just plain tofu, chopped in small chunks.
3 cups chopped, steamed vegetables
Include:
1 cup mushrooms or onions
1 cup broccoli, green peppers or zucchini
1 cup carrots or small yellow squash
1-2 recipes for CURRY SAUCE

1 avocado, sliced in thin strips
2-4 tomatoes, sliced in thin wedges

Directions

Spread the hot cooked grain in a one inch or so thick layer on a warmed serving platter.

Next layer the tofu followed by the mixed, steamed vegetables. Top it off with the curry sauce, covering the centre and dribbling down the sides of the "mountain".

Decorate the top and sides with avocado slices and tomato or carrot pieces. Put leftover curry sauce in a gravy server as people usually like extra sauce. Keep the platter in a warm oven until serving. Leftovers reheat easily in a covered pan with a little water on low heat. Keeps 4-6 days refrigerated.

T
O
F
U

Mild Curry Sauce

Ingredients

3 Tbsp. light oil
6 Tbsp. whole wheat flour

3½ cups low-fat milk or soy milk
   or cashew milk
1-2 tsp. curry powder
½ - 1 tsp. turmeric
1 tsp. sea salt
Several dashes cayenne red
   pepper

Optional: 1-2 tsp. honey or liquid sweetener to balance flavours

Directions

Heat the oil in a frying pan until melted and hot over medium-high heat. Sprinkle on the flour and stir it over a low flame until it is browned and crumbly. Take care it doesn't burn.

Then add the milk and seasonings and stir it over a medium to low heat until it thickens into a sauce. Correct seasonings according to taste. Keep covered and hot until serving. Keeps refrigerated for 5-7 days.

Yield: 4 cups (32 oz.)

TOFU

Tofu-Stuffed Zucchini

Ingredients

4-6 small zucchini, cut in half
  lengthwise, remove ends

2 Tbsp. oil
2-3 green onions, diced
½ cup green pepper, chopped
  fine
7-8 mushrooms, chopped (or ⅓
  cup diced eggplant, pre-
  sautéed)

14-16 oz. tofu
2-3 tsp. tamari soy sauce
½ tsp. sea salt
½ tsp. curry powder
Several dashes cayenne red
  pepper

Optional: several dashes
turmeric for a yellow colour

Yield: 4-6 servings

Directions

Steam the zucchini for 4-7 minutes until slightly tender.

In a frying pan, heat the oil and saute the onions, pepper and mushrooms for a couple of minutes.

Add the tofu and remaining ingredients (except zucchini) and saute for a few minutes more until the flavours mingle. Place the strips of zucchini, centre side up in a low baking dish with about ¼"or a bit more of water in the bottom. Cover the zucchini with the tofu mixture, taking care not to spill any in the water. Bake for 10-15 minutes until everything is hot and tender throughout. Serve immediately as a main dish with a whole grain. Keeps refrigerated 3-5 days.

T
O
F
U

Vegetable and Tofu Shish Kebabs

Ingredients

Use ¼ - ¾ inch pieces about 1-2 inches long of several of the following vegetables and foods: (Use about 2 cups per person.)

Pineapple, in chunks
Citrus slices
Green, red or yellow peppers, in 1-1½ inch chunks
Zucchini, in ¼ inch thick rounds
Mushrooms, small whole or cut in half
Potatoes, in 1 inch chunks (pre-steamed 10 minutes)
Cauliflower, in 1½ inch chunks (pre-steamed 5 minutes)
Tomatoes, in 1½ - 2 inch chunks
TOFU CUTLETS or tofu from RICE ROLL-UPS, in chunks (see other tofu recipes)
Onions, in wedges
Edible pea pods

Use one or more of these sauces:
Garlic French Dressing
Thousand Island Dressing
Barbeque Sauce
Tomato Sauce – ¾ part mixed with ¼ part tamari soy sauce or dark miso
Tamari soy sauce by itself, poured over kebabs

Yield: serves 6

Directions

Use two or more bamboo or stainless steel skewers about 1 foot long per person. Select a variety of vegetables and tofu. Place the foods on the spears alternately, filling each spear completely. Use a cooking brush to baste the kebabs with the sauce(s). Use only one type of sauce per each separate kebab and baste each one generously. Broil the kebabs for 4-10 minutes, (depending on your broiler type), until tender and juicy. Serve immediately before they cool. Serve over brown rice, millet, quinoa, buckwheat, kasha or another whole grain. Use the juices from the broiling pan on the grains for added flavour.

TOFU

Rice Salad Roll-ups with Tofu

Ingredients

Tofu Sauté:

½ - 1 lb. tofu, cut in french fry shaped strips
2 tsp. oil
2-4 Tbsp. tamari soy sauce
Several dashes cayenne red pepper

Extra Ingredients:

Tahini Sauce, 1 batch - hot or cold (see below)
1 pkg. large, round, rice wrappers (available in Oriental stores)
1-2 cups Mung bean sprouts, washed
1 cup or more mung or Chinese noodles or brown rice, pre-cooked
1-2 red peppers, cut in thin strips
3-9 lettuce or spinach leaves, cut in strips or shredded
1 bunch of green onions, whole, cleaned and trimmed
Optional: a couple of carrots, grated

Directions

Cut the tofu in strips the size of thin, ¼" wide french fries. Heat the 2 tsp. of oil in a small skillet and add the tofu strips. Sauté one minute and add the tamari soy sauce and cayenne pepper. Sauté another minute and set aside to cool or leave hot for the rice roll-ups.

Take two, extra large, paper thin, rice wrappers together and dip them in warm, not hot water, for 30 seconds or so to soften them. Lay them on a clean, flat surface and start placing the extra ingredients on the lower middle of the wrappers. Use about 1 tablespoon each of the mung sprouts and noodles or rice. Add several strips of peppers, leafy greens and a bit of carrot if used. Lay the ingredients in a horizontal line, a couple

CONTINUED NEXT PAGE

T
O
F
U

of inches from the bottom of the wrapper. Fold in the right and left sides of the wrapper and tuck a green onion's white bulb under one of the folds, letting the green top stick out over the other folded side. Then from the bottom, roll up the wrapper as tightly as possible without tearing it. It rolls up just like a burrito. Dip one end of the roll-up in the Tahini Sauce and enjoy, dipping the roll-up in extra sauce before each bite. Enjoy 2-3 roll-ups as a complete lunch or supper. Eliminate the onions if you have trouble digesting raw onions.

T
O
F
U

Tahini Sauce

Ingredients

1 cup chopped onion
2-3 cloves garlic, minced
2 Tbsp. light oil or butter

1 cup sesame tahini
1 Tbsp. liquid sweetener
¼ cup lemon juice
2 tsp. grated ginger
2 bay leaves
1 Tbsp. apple cider vinegar
2 cups water
1 tsp. tamari soy sauce
½ - 1 tsp. sea salt
Several dashes cayenne/red
    pepper to taste

Directions

Sauté the onions and garlic in
the oil until tender.

Add all the remaining ingredients. Mix thoroughly. Simmer on
very low heat for 20-30 minutes
until hot throughout and
flavours have mingled.

Serve over hot vegetables, whole
grains or rice roll-ups. Keeps 6-8
days refrigerated or may be
frozen.

Yield: 28 oz.

T
O
F
U

Tofu Cutlets

Ingredients

2-3 lbs. pressed or regular tofu, (pressed is preferable)

4 cups water or vegetable stock
⅔ cup tamari soy sauce
2 Tbsp. chili powder*
1 Tbsp. onion powder*
1 Tbsp. garlic powder*
½ tsp. sea kelp
Several dashes cayenne red pepper

* Chili powder can be eliminated if necessary by using one of the variations. Onion and/or garlic powder can be eliminated with little or more loss of flavour, if necessary, in any of the three variations.

Yield: 2-3 pounds

Directions

Pre-freeze the tofu, then defrost in warm water until thawed. Freezing texturizes the tofu and helps separate out some of the water. Gently hand press as much water as possible from the tofu. Slice it into ¼ inch thick slabs and cut these into 1½ - 2 inch pieces. Press them dry with paper towels.

Mix all the remaining ingredients, except the tofu, together in a pot twice the size and bring it to a boil, stirring occasionally. When it boils, lower the heat and let it simmer, covered for 12-15 minutes or more. Then add the tofu pieces and let it simmer together for an additional 30 minutes so the flavours can be absorbed into the tofu pieces. Stir the liquid occasionally and turn the tofu pieces.

CONTINUED NEXT PAGE

T
O
F
U

Then remove the tofu from the liquid and serve hot as a snack or side dish or added to recipes. The tofu cutlets can be eaten hot from the pot, cold or broiled for a few minutes on each side. Cold, they can be eaten on the run as an occasional, nutritious "meal replacement". Cold, they can also be eaten like hors d'oeuvres with toothpicks or sliced on sandwiches or crackers as canapes. They can be used instead of meat in many recipes. Crumble them in tomato sauce or lasagna. Use pieces in stir fried vegetables, tempura, shish kebabs, casseroles, rice dishes or in many other main dish recipes. When broiled, they have a succulent, unique flavour that even surpasses their delicious-ness when served in the hot or cold methods mentioned above. Enjoy this wholesome treat often! (Serve with a whole grain whenever possible.) Store left over tofu in glass containers up to 1-2 weeks in the refrigerator or freeze for up to 3 months in individual serving sizes stored in plastic bags for easy access. Try variations:

Curried Tofu Cutlets

Eliminate the chili powder from the above recipe and add: 2-3 tsp. curry powder and ½ tsp turmeric. Optional: ¼ tsp. each of cumin and coriander.

Green Herb Cutlets

Eliminate the chili powder from the above recipe and add: 1 Tbsp. parsley flakes and 1 tsp. basil. Also add ¼ tsp. each: oregano and marjoram.

T
O
F
U

Carob Mint Tofu Pudding

Ingredients

1 lb. soft tofu (use regular tofu if soft is unavailable)
1 - 1½ cups maple syrup, honey or fruit concentrate
½ - ⅔ cup carob powder
2 Tbsp. arrowroot powder
3 tsp. natural vanilla flavouring
¼ tsp. or bit more peppermint extract
Few dashes sea salt

Directions

Use a food processor or homogenizing juicer to mix all the ingredients. (This pudding is too thick for a blender.) Put in individual pudding cups and chill thoroughly. A rich dessert.

T
O
F
U

Yield: 4 servings

Almond Carob Tofu Pudding

Ingredients

1 lb. soft tofu
1 - 1½ cups maple syrup
⅓ - ⅔ cup carob powder
¼ cup almond butter
2 Tbsp. arrowroot powder
3 tsp. natural vanilla flavour
¹⁄₁₆ - ¼ tsp. almond extract
Few dashes sea salt

Extra: ½ cup slivered almonds plus extra slivered almonds

Directions

Prepare the same as the *Carob Mint Tofu Pudding* above. After processing, mix ½ cup slivered almonds to the finished pudding before chilling. Sprinkle a few more slivered almonds on top of each serving. Keeps 5-8 days refrigerated.

Yield: 4 servings

T
O
F
U

Easy Tofu Fruit Parfaits

Ingredients

2 large kiwis, peeled and sliced
1 lb. soft tofu (use regular tofu, crumbled, if unavailable)
⅔ - ¾ cup honey or maple syrup
2 Tbsp. arrowroot powder
1 tsp. natural vanilla flavouring

Optional: 1-2 tsp. guar gum thickener

2-4 extra kiwis, peeled and sliced ⅛ inch thick
Granola or other crunchy-nut cereal

Yield: 4-6 servings

Directions

Blend or use a food processor to mix the tofu with the 2 kiwis and the remaining first ingredients. Put 1-inch or more of the mixture in a parfait glass.

Next, layer 2 layers of sliced kiwis and/or a ½"–1" layer of granola or cereal. Then add another 1 inch or more of the kiwi-tofu mixture. Continue rotating the layers until the top of the glass is topped with kiwi-tofu mixture. Top it all off with a sprinkle of cereal and a ¼" round of kiwi stuck horizontally halfway into the topping. Chill thoroughly in the refrigerator and enjoy as a light but nourishing dessert. The guar gum makes a firmer fruit parfait similar to one using gelatin. Without it, the parfait is more pudding-like and a softer texture is achieved. Keeps 2-4 days refrigerated. Try these variations:

CONTINUED NEXT PAGE

TOFU

Variations:

Strawberry-Tofu Parfait -
Blend 1 ½ cups strawberries
instead of kiwis into the above
recipe. Slice another 1-2 cups
for layering.

Blueberry-Tofu Parfait - Blend
1 ½ cups blueberries instead of
kiwis into the above recipe.
Leave another 1-2 cups whole
for layering.

**Pineapple-Coconut-Tofu
Parfait** - Use 1 ½ cups crushed
or blended pineapple instead of
kiwis in the above recipe. Use
another 1-2 cups crushed or
chunk pineapple for layering.
Unsweetened shredded coconut
can also be layered and sprin-
kled on top.

Other Fruit to Try: peaches,
mangos, bananas, raspberries.

T
O
F
U

Tofu Cheesecake

Ingredients

1 ½ lbs. (24 oz.) soft (or regular) tofu
1 cup honey, maple syrup or fruit concentrate
¼ cup natural raw sugar (use if possible or use white sugar)
3 Tbsp. oil
3 Tbsp. arrowroot powder
2 Tbsp. lemon juice
1 Tbsp. lemon rind, finely grated
1 Tbsp. vanilla extract
⅛ - ¼ tsp. sea salt

Optional: 1 pie crust recipe

Directions

Use a food processor or homogenizing juicer to mix all the ingredients together well. Use a 9" pie plate if no crust is used. Use a 10" pie plate for a crust. Oil the pie pan or prepare the crust and spread the tofu mixture inside. Smooth out the top so the "cheese" cake will be even. Bake in a pre-heated oven at 350° for about 45 minutes, more or less until set and a dark, golden colour. Chill thoroughly and serve with strawberry or other fruit topping and enjoy.

T
O
F
U

Yield: 9–12 servings

Carob Tofu Cheesecake

Ingredients

22 oz. soft (or regular) tofu
¾ cup liquid sweetener
½ cup roasted carob powder
⅓ cup natural raw sugar or barley malt powder
3 Tbsp. oil
3 Tbsp. arrowroot powder
2 Tbsp. lemon juice
1 Tbsp. vanilla extract
⅛ - ¼ tsp. sea salt

Optional: 1/16 - ¼ tsp. peppermint extract

Optional: 1 pie crust recipe

Directions

Prepare the same as *Tofu Cheesecake*.

Yield: 9–12 servings

T
O
F
U

Strawberry Topping for Tofu Cheesecake

Ingredients

½ lb. fresh or frozen strawberries
   or other fruit*
1 cup water
2-3 Tbsp. arrowroot powder
2-3 Tbsp. liquid sweetener

* Try blackberries, raspberries, blueberries, peach slices or other fruit instead of strawberries if desired. Keeps up to 7-8 days refrigerated.

Directions

Heat the strawberries in ½ cup of the water. Mash the strawberries as they heat or pre-slice them. Mix the other ½ cup water thoroughly with the arrowroot powder. Add the arrowroot mixture and sweetener to the strawberries and stir constantly over medium heat until the sauce becomes bright red and thickens. Chill before using on the "Cheese" cake or on other dessert recipes.

T O F U

Yield: 1 ½ cups

Tofu Fruit Smoothie

Ingredients

1 small basket of strawberries
   (approximately 2 cups)
2 large bananas, frozen*
4 oz. tofu
⅛ - ¼ cup liquid sweetener
2-3 tsp. vanilla flavouring

* Either the strawberries or the bananas should be pre-frozen to ensure a cool temperature for the drink after blending.

Directions

Blend all ingredients thoroughly and serve immediately. Other frozen fruits may be used to create different drinks. Try: blueberries, raspberries, peaches, pears, apricots, kiwi, mangos and others. Dates or other dried fruits can also be used to help sweeten the drink along with nut milk or other flavoured milks.

Yield: 4 cups

T
O
F
U

Tofu Whipped Cream

Ingredients

6-8 oz. very fresh regular or soft
tofu (lightly steamed if
desired)

4-6 Tbsp. maple syrup, or to
taste

1-2 tsp. natural vanilla flavouring

Optional: 1-2 dashes cinnamon

Directions

Rinse the tofu in cold water and
press out all the water possible
by squeezing it between several
layers of paper towelling. Break
the tofu into small pieces and
put it in the food processor with
the remaining ingredients.
Process and then taste the mixture. Adjust the flavourings if
desired. Chill and serve. ¼ cup
fruit jam or spread may also be
added to make *Tofruity Whipped
Cream*. Keeps 2-5 days refrigerated.

TOFU

Yield: 4 servings

TOFU

CHAPTER
5

Terrific Vegetables & Meatless Dishes

VEGETABLES

Fruit-Filled Squash Rings
MICROWAVEABLE

Ingredients

1 small acorn squash

½ cup chopped apple with skin
1 Tbsp. brown sugar
½ tsp. fresh lemon juice
3 Tbsp. chopped walnuts
½ cup cranberry sauce, whole
  berry
2 tsp. cornstarch

Zest of 1 lemon

Directions

Wash squash, pierce skin several times with a fork. Microwave on High 4-6 minutes till soft and yields slightly to pressure. Let stand 1 minute.

Combine remaining ingredients except zest of lemon, in a small microwaveable casserole dish, cover and cook on High 2-4 minutes, stirring occasionally. Cut squash into ½" rings. Remove seeds and fibers. Place rings on a large microwaveable plate and fill with fruit sauce. Cook an additional 3-5 minutes uncovered on High till squash is tender throughout.

Garnish with lemon zest.

Yield: 3 servings

This recipe submitted by Gale Larabee

Cal 215   Fat 5.6

Asparagus Loaf

Ingredients

½ cup cracker crumbs, finely
ground
2 cups cooked asparagus,
drained and cut lengthwise
into 1 inch pieces
1 cup 1% milk
1 egg plus 2 egg whites, slightly
beaten
2 Tbsp. margarine
1 tsp. salt
1 tsp. grated onion

Directions

Mix all ingredients together.
Bake in a non-stick coated baking dish in moderate oven. May
be served with 2 cups of tomato
sauce mixed with ½ cup of
chopped parsley.

Yield: 4 servings

Cal 135   Fat 8 g

VEGETABLES

Eggplant Parmigiana

Ingredients

1 medium eggplant
Olive oil

1 8-oz. can Italian light tomato
  sauce
6 oz. grated low-fat partly
  skimmed mozzarella cheese

Directions

Slice eggplant (peel if desired) in
¼ inch slices. Brush very lightly
with oil. Bake on non-stick cookie sheet in 400° oven. Turn
once when brown.

Cover the bottom of a baking
dish with a small amount of
sauce. Alternate layers of baked
eggplant, sauce and cheese.
Bake at 350° for ½ hour.

Yield: 6 servings

Cal 122   Fat 9.3 g

Zucchini Delight

Ingredients

1 large zucchini

Fresh or dried basil and oregano
2 medium ripe tomatoes, sliced
2 cups skim ricotta cheese
4 oz. part skim mozzarella
    cheese, grated

Yield: 4 servings

Directions

Slice the zucchini. Fry in non-stick fry pan lightly coated with cooking spray, until lightly brown on each side. (Total browning approximately 10 minutes).

Spray a baking dish with cooking spray. Fill the dish with alternating layers of sliced tomatoes, zucchini, ricotta cheese and grated mozzarella. End with mozzarella. Sprinkle a few pinches of basil and oregano on top. Bake 10-15 minutes in 400° oven until casserole begins to bubble around the edges. Serve while hot.

Variation: Use eggplant instead of zucchini.

It's easy to make two small casseroles and freeze the extra one, well covered, for future use.

Cal 234   Fat 12 g

Sautéed Caraway Cabbage

Ingredients

1 head cabbage (2 lbs.)
4 cups water
1 tsp. salt
1 Bay leaf
2 whole cloves

1 Tbsp. and 1 tsp. margarine
½ cup thinly sliced onion

⅓ cup and 2 tsp. chicken broth

Dash of pepper
½ tsp. caraway seeds

Yield: 4 servings

Directions

Wash and trim cabbage, cut into 4 wedges. In saucepan bring water to a boil and add salt, bay leaf, cloves and cabbage. Boil for about 15 minutes or until tender; drain.

Melt margarine in non-stick skillet. Add onion slices and saute briefly. Add cabbage, cut-side down, being careful not to break wedges. Sauté until lightly browned; turn and sauté other cut side.

Add broth and simmer until most of the liquid has been absorbed.

Season with pepper, then sprinkle with caraway seeds.

Cal 100   Fat 2 g

Red or Green Cabbage

Ingredients

1 medium cabbage, coarsely
   chopped
1 leek
3 garlic cloves

1 Tsp. olive oil (optional)
½ lemon (optional)

Directions

Rinse vegetables in cold water.
Steam cabbage, leek and garlic.
Add oil and lemon (if desired).

Yield: 4 servings

Cal 99   Fat 1.6 g

VEGETABLES

Preparation of
Corn on the Cob

Ingredients

4 fresh cobs of corn
Water

Directions

Prepare corn as fresh as possible.

Place a few tablespoons of water in pot and bring to a boil.

Shut off the heat. Cover bottom of pot with a few corn husks.

Place shucked corn on top of husks, cover and steam for 3 minutes.

Remove and eat immediately. Serve with light butter or margarine if desired.

Yield: 4 servings

Calories and fat per cob, without butter.

Cal 150   Fat 1 g

Vegetable Kebabs

Ingredients

4 fresh mushrooms, halved
1 medium green pepper, cut
    into 1 inch squares
1 summer squash, cut into ½
    inch slices
8 cherry tomatoes

Directions

In a bowl pour boiling water over mushrooms and green pepper. Let stand 1 minute; drain. On four skewers alternately thread mushrooms, green pepper squares, summer squash and cherry tomatoes. Place on unheated rack in broiler pan. Broil 4 inches from heat about 10 minutes or till heated through, turning occasionally.

Yield: 4 servings

Cal 22   Fat 0 g

Oven-Baked Sweet Potatoes

Ingredients

3 large sweet potatoes
3 large Yukon gold potatoes
½ cup water
2 Tbsp. olive oil
2 tsp. dried rosemary

Directions

Peel potatoes; slice ⅛ inch thick. In 13 x 9 inch baking dish, pack sweet and white potatoes tightly in alternating rows; sprinkle evenly with water. Drizzle with half of the oil; and sprinkle with rosemary. Bake, covered, in 325° oven for 1 hour and 10 minutes. Uncover, baste with remaining oil and broil for 3 to 5 minutes or until crisp and brown on top.

Yield: 8 servings

Cal 120   Fat 4 g

Fresh Mushroom Rice

Ingredients

2 cups chicken bouillon
1 cup white rice

2 tsp. margarine
2 whole green onions, thinly sliced
6 large mushrooms, finely chopped

Directions

Bring bouillon to a boil in a medium-size saucepan. Add rice. Cover and reduce heat to low. Cook for 20 to 25 minutes.

In a small frying pan sauté onions and mushrooms in margarine for 5 minutes. Toss with hot cooked rice. Add salt and pepper to taste.

Yield: 4 servings

Cal 245   Fat 2 g

VEGETABLES

How to Prepare Brown Rice

Ingredients

2 cups brown rice

Water

Directions

Wash the rice by pouring cold water over two cups of brown rice until any dust rises to the surface of the water. Drain water, and repeat if necessary until no more appears.

Add 3 cups of water to the clean rice and bring to a boil quickly. Cover pot, and boil slowly for 45 minutes or until water is absorbed. Do not lift lid until time is up. Turn off heat, and let steam for 10 minutes.

Keep the rice in the refrigerator, and reheat it at mealtime.

Yield: 4 servings

Cal 230

Fat "tr"

How to Make
Brown Rice Pudding

Ingredients

2 tsp. of apple cider vinegar
¼ cup raisins
2 cups of cooked rice
2 egg whites
1¾ cups skim milk
Dash of cinnamon and nutmeg

Directions

Add apple cider vinegar to raisins. Set aside to plump. Stir cooked rice into egg whites and milk. Mix well. Stir in raisins and a little cinnamon and nutmeg. Cook at low heat and stir periodically for about ½ hour, until thick.

Keep unused portion in the refrigerator and reheat as you desire.

Yield: 4 servings

Cal 256   Fat trace

VEGETABLES

Speedy Oatmeal Hamburgers

Ingredients

1 cup oatmeal, dry
1 tsp. salt substitute
1 tsp. sage

1 medium onion, chopped finely

6 egg whites

1 2-oz. can mushroom gravy
1 4-oz. low-sodium tomato
  sauce

Yield: 6 servings

Directions

Mix oats, salt and sage in bowl.

Combine onion and oats and shape into patties.

Beat eggs until frothy. Stir oat mixture into eggs quickly and fry in hot oil, just long enough to brown lightly on both sides. Remove at once to warm plate.

When all are fried, place in pan again and cover with a tomato-mushroom sauce. Simmer for 20 minutes to ½ hour. Great served hot or cold.

Cal 115   Fat 1.5 g

Buckwheat Casserole

Ingredients

1 cup buckwheat groats
2 cups water

Optional:
1 carrot
1 stalk celery
¼ green or red pepper
1 leek

Directions

Soak buckwheat groats overnight. Rinse buckwheat groats and cover with fresh water. Bring to boil. Turn to medium heat and when steaming shut off heat and let sit 10-15 minutes. Serve with fresh dill and unsalted margarine.

Variation: Thinly sliced vegetables. Steam on top of buckwheat.

Yield: 4 servings

Cal 164   Fat "tr"

VEGETABLES

Barbequed Tofu

Ingredients

8 oz. tofu, firm pressed

Onion powder to taste
¼ tsp. Spike or Mrs. Dash
1 tsp. low-sodium soy sauce

Directions

Slice pressed tofu into 4 large slices, approximately 1" thick. Press again, with more weight, changing absorbent towels frequently. Tofu should be very firm.

Sprinkle with seasonings and soy sauce on both sides of each slice. Place over hot coals and grill until each side is lightly browned. Smoke flavoring from the coals is very apparent in contrast to the mild taste of tofu.

Yield: 4 servings

Cal 45   Fat 1 g

Tofu "Patties"

Ingredients

6 oz. tofu, firm pressed
1 egg

1 Wasa Bread (Light Rye),
    crushed finely
1 tsp. onion flakes
1 tsp. celery flakes
¼ tsp. garlic powder
½ small green pepper, finely
    minced
¼ tsp. black pepper
1 Tbsp. bacon bits (optional)
¼ cup alfalfa sprouts, minced

Directions

Mash tofu and egg together very well.

Add remaining ingredients. Form 2 large patties. Preheat non-stick pan over medium-heat. (You may need to use some non-stick cooking spray in addition to avoid sticking.) Cook patties until lightly browned on each side.

Yield: 2 servings

Cal 99   Fat "tr"

VEGETABLES

Scrambled Tofu

Ingredients

8 oz. tofu, unpressed
½ tsp. turmeric powder
¼ tsp. garlic powder
¼ tsp. black pepper
Spike or Mrs. Dash to taste

Directions

Preheat non-stick pan over medium heat. Stirring constantly, crumble tofu into pan and add seasonings. Tofu heats very fast, making it puffy and slightly golden.

Yield: 4 servings

Cal 41

Fat 1 g

"Fried" Tofu and "Fried" Eggs

Ingredients

4 oz. tofu, pressed; cut in 2 slices
2 Tbsp. unprocessed bran

2 eggs
4 drops soy sauce in 2 tsp. water
Pepper to taste

Directions

Coat the tofu slices with bran. Very lightly pat the tofu with fingers to press the bran into tofu. If all the bran doesn't stick to the tofu, dip and pat again. Coat skillet with non-stick cooking spray. Cook the tofu over medium heat until browned on one side. Turn over.

Break one egg over each slice of tofu. Cover pan for 2 minutes to lightly "steam" the eggs. Pour half the soy sauce in water over each egg. Sprinkle with pepper. Cover pan and cook until eggs are done to your taste.

Yield: 2 servings

Cal 185   Fat 1.3 g

Tamale Pie

Ingredients

1 cup 1% milk
1 tsp. salt substitute

¾ cup corn chips

1 egg, slightly beaten
1 ½ cups corn niblets

1 onion, chopped
½ cup green pepper, chopped

2 cups stewed tomatoes
Pinch of garlic salt

Directions

Combine milk and salt. Heat milk up to just boiling.

Combine corn chips with hot milk and stir until smooth.

Add egg and corn to mixture and stir well.

Sauté onion and pepper in non-stick frypan coated with cooking spray.

Add tomatoes and garlic and bring to a boil. Combine with corn mixture and pour into a casserole. Bake at 350° for 30 minutes.

Yield: 6 servings

Cal 219

Fat 4 g

Tortilla Pizza

MICROWAVEABLE

Try this versatile tortilla base "pizza" with your favourite low-cal toppings.

Ingredients

1 8-inch tortilla

2 Tbsp. low-sodium tomato paste
2 Tbsp. partly-skimmed mozzarella cheese, grated
1 slice Canadian-style bacon or pepperoni, diced
⅓ cup fresh mushrooms, sliced
Seasonings to taste (basil & oregano)

Directions

Place tortilla between 2 double-thick layers of paper towels. Microwave on High for 1 minute or until crisp. Remove top layer of paper towel.

Spread tortilla with 2 tablespoons tomato paste. Sprinkle with remaining ingredients. Microwave pizza 1½ minutes more or until cheese topping is bubbly.

If you prefer, you can toast the pizza in a 425° oven for five minutes.

Yield: 1 serving

Cal 225   Fat 6 g

VEGETABLES

Quick and Easy Pizza

Enjoy with fresh salad or favourite raw veggies.

Ingredients

1 medium pizza shell or dough mix

1½ cups pizza sauce
1½ cups low-fat cottage cheese

1 small green pepper (cut into julienne strips)
1 small red pepper (cut into julienne strips)
1 small onion, sliced thinly
7 mushrooms, sliced
Sprinkle italian spices to taste
Freshly ground pepper
4 Tbsp. grated low-fat mozzarella cheese

Yield: 8 slices

Directions

Preheat oven to 500°. On a lightly floured surface, roll dough into a 10-inch circle. Place on a 10-inch pizza pan.

Mix pizza sauce and cottage cheese together. Spread over crust.

Arrange peppers, onions and mushrooms over dough then sprinkle with spices and top sparingly with mozzarella cheese.

Bake on bottom rack of preheated oven for 15-18 minutes or until crust starts to turn golden colour when edges are lifted up gently.

Cal 330   Fat 5.2 g

Mushroom, Broccoli and Onion Pizza

Keep some homemade or store-bought pizza dough rounds in your freezer so you can easily make your own fast food.

Depending on the toppings you choose, your pizzas can be nutritious as well as delicious.

Ingredients

1 round (12-inch) pizza dough

½ cup tomato sauce
1 tsp. dried oregano (or 2 Tbsp. fresh)
½ tsp. dried basil (or 1 Tbsp. fresh)

10 mushrooms, sliced
1 onion, sliced
3 cups small broccoli florets
½ sweet red and/or yellow pepper, chopped

2½ cups shredded low-fat mozzarella cheese
pinch red pepper flakes

Yield: 4 servings
(2 pieces each)

Directions

Place pizza dough on baking sheet.

Combine tomato sauce, oregano and basil; mix well and spread over pizza dough.

Arrange mushrooms, broccoli, onion and red pepper on top.

Sprinkle with cheese and red pepper flakes, if using. Bake in 475° oven for 12 minutes or until cheese is bubbling. Cut into 8 pieces.

Calories and fat per two-piece serving:

Cal 424   Fat 16 g

Macaroni and Cheese

Ingredients

2 cups grated low-fat Cheddar cheese (reserve ½ cup for topping)

2 cups whole wheat macaroni, cooked

¾ cup evaporated skim milk

2 Tbsp. finely chopped onion

2 Tbsp. chopped fresh parsley

1 tsp. salt (optional)

¼ tsp. pepper

Paprika (for topping)

Variations: Chopped green pepper gives colour and crunchiness. Also try 1 cup of tomato sauce in place of the skim milk for a tasty flavour.

Directions

Combine ingredients in a shallow casserole dish sprayed with non-stick cooking oil. Top with remaining cheese and sprinkle with paprika. Broil in oven for five minutes until light brown.

Yield: 6 servings

Cal 239.2   Fat 7 g

Six Quick Macaroni Variations

Italian
Toss 2 cups hot cooked macaroni with 4 tablespoons chopped sun-dried tomatoes, 1 tablespoon parmesan and ½ tsp. basil. Serves 4.

Lemon
Stir 2 cups hot cooked macaroni with 2 tablespoons butter, 2 tablespoons chopped parsley, grated peel of 1 lemon, 2 teaspoons lemon juice and freshly ground black pepper. Serves 4.

Mediterranean
Place 4 cups cooked macaroni, 6 oz. drained and quartered marinated artichokes and 14 oz. chopped drained plum tomatoes in a wide saucepan. Stir over medium heat. When hot, add 2 cups grated partly skimmed mozzarella. Serves 8.

Spinach
Saute a 300 gram package of chopped spinach and 1 crushed garlic clove in 1 tablespoon of olive oil. When hot, add 2 cups cooked macaroni and sprinkle slightly with grated Swiss cheese. Stir until hot. Serves 4.

Stuffed Peppers
Stir 2 cups cooked macaroni with 1 cup grated low-fat cheddar cheese, 2 chopped canned tomatoes and 1 tsp. Italian herb seasoning. Spoon mixture into 4 green pepper halves. Bake at 375° for 20 minutes. Serves 2.

Vegetable
Sauté 1 shredded zucchini in 1 tablespoon melted margarine for 2 minutes. Add 3 cups cooked macaroni, ¼ cup parmesan and a pinch of nutmeg. Stir until hot. Serves 4.

VEGETABLES

Rotini with Fresh Tomatoes, Basil and Parmesan

You can use any kind of pasta in this easy recipe. To preserve the tomatoes' fresh flavour and texture, cook quickly over high heat. Once the pasta is ready, the whole mixture cooks in less than five minutes.

Ingredients

½ lb. rotini (corkscrew shape) or any tubular pasta

2 Tbsp. vegetable oil
4 green onions, chopped
4 tomatoes, coarsely chopped
3 cloves garlic, minced

1 cup strips or cubes cooked ham, turkey, chicken (optional)
¼ cup coarsely chopped fresh basil (or 1 tsp. dried)
1 cup coarsely chopped fresh parsley
½ cup grated parmesan cheese
Salt and pepper

Yield: 4 servings

Directions

In a large pot of boiling water, cook pasta until *al dente* (tender but firm); drain. (If sauce isn't ready, rinse pasta under warm water for a few seconds to prevent it sticking together).

Meanwhile, in large heavy saucepan or Dutch oven, heat oil over high heat. Add onions, tomatoes and garlic; cook, stirring, for 2 to 3 minutes or until tomatoes are just heated through but still hold their shape.

Stir in rotini, ham (if using), parsley, basil and parmesan. Reduce heat to medium; cook, stirring gently, for about 2 minutes or until heated through. Season with salt and pepper to taste.

Fat and calories for meatless version.

Cal 368   Fat 11 g

Spaghetti with Sweet Peppers and Mushrooms

Ingredients

Cooking spray
1 onion, diced
1 bay leaf

⅔ cup chicken stock
3 green peppers, thinly sliced
1 cup mushrooms, sliced
2 cloves garlic, minced
3 Tbsp. fresh Italian parsley, minced
1 tsp. dried basil
½ tsp. dried thyme
½ tsp. dried oregano

2 cups cooked whole wheat spaghetti (4 oz. dry)

Directions

Coat a large non-stick frying pan with cooking spray. Add onion and bay leaf. Saute about 5 minutes.

Add stock, peppers, mushrooms, garlic, parsley, basil, thyme and oregano. Simmer uncovered, 5 to 7 minutes, or until peppers are soft and the liquid has reduced slightly.

Remove bay leaf. Add cooked spaghetti. Toss and re-heat. Serve hot.

Yield: 4 servings

Cal 143   Fat 1 g

VEGETABLES

Spinach Lasagna

Ingredients

1 10-oz. package frozen
   chopped spinach, cooked
1 lb. lasagna noodles, cooked,
   drained & rinsed

1 medium onion, chopped
½ green pepper, chopped
Cooking spray

2 1-lb. cans of tomatoes
1 6-oz. can tomato paste

1 Tbsp. oregano flakes
1 Tbsp. basil
1 bay leaf
½ tsp. salt
¼ cup fresh parsley, chopped

1 lb. low-fat 1% cottage cheese
8 oz. low-fat mozzarella cheese,
   shredded or in thin slices
3 Tbsp. parmesan cheese
2 egg whites

Optional: ⅓ cup grated carrots
if tomatoes are bitter

Yield: 10 servings

Directions

Set cooked noodles and spinach aside separately.

Sauté onion and pepper in non-stick frypan coated with cooking spray.

Add tomatoes and paste to onions. Break up larger tomato pieces.

Add seasonings, stir and simmer 30 minutes.

Combine cottage cheese and egg whites to chopped spinach and mix well. Cover bottom of 9 x 13" baking dish with ⅓ of tomato sauce. Cover with ⅓ the noodle strips, half the spinach mixture and half of mozzarella. Spread one third more of tomato sauce and repeat layers and topping with noodles and remaining tomato sauce. Sprinkle with parmesan cheese. Bake at 350° for 40 minutes.

Cal 159   Fat 3.9 g

Meat and Seafood Dishes

Chicken
1. Citrus Chicken Breasts
2. Cranberry-Orange Chicken
3. Szechuan Orange-Ginger Chicken
4. Oriental Chicken
5. Southern Fried Chicken Strips
6. Peppery Chicken Stir-Fry
7. Chicken Chili
8. Orange Chicken Oriental
9. Tandoori Chicken
10. Chicken-Greek Style
11. Orange-Mustard Chicken
12. Spicy Baked Chicken
13. Chicken Paprikash

Turkey
14. Goulash (Turkey) Viennese
15. Westerner's Chili
16. Turkey Broccoli Bake
17. Country-Style Turkey
18. Peppery Turkey Slices
19. Turkey Cutlets
20. Turkey Pasta Salad
21. Citrus Turkey with Rice
22. Spicy Lamb Chili
23. Glazed Orange Pork
24. Pork à l'Orange
25. Sliced Steak Sandwich
26. Swiss Steak

Seafood
28. Oriental Tuna Stir-Fry
29. Fish Portuguese
30. Sole Florentine
31. Poached Fish with Dill Sauce
32. Baked Red Snapper
33. Shrimp Newberg
34. Crustless Crabmeat and Vegetable Pie
35. Ribbon-Skewered Halibut
36. Halibut Italian-Style

Meat & Seafood Tips

Here are some ways to reduce fat intake without feeling deprived or making great sacrifices in your eating or cooking style.

Recipes can become low-fat with some smart substitutions like these.

1. Instead of fatty cuts of meats as ribs and chops, choose lean ones like beef round, lambs, pork loin, any beef "tips" and skinless poultry.

2. Baste meats with fruit juice, marinate meats in wine and herbs, serve fish with fresh squeezed lemon instead of gravies and sauces.

3. Sauté foods in broth instead of oil.

4. Top chicken breasts, fish or vegetables with grated parmesan cheese, chopped sun dried tomatoes, and use soy sauce (with garlic and ginger) or tomato sauce instead of fattening butter.

5. After you roast meat or poultry, chill the drippings in the refrigerator. Once cooled, the fat will rise to the top and harden; you can remove it easily and save the stock for future stews, sauces and soups.

6. Water- or broth-packed tuna will save you 74 calories per 7-oz. can.

7. Use partly skimmed mozzarella in place of cheddar for pastas. The mozzarella has 118 calories per 1½ oz.; cheddar has 181.

8. Spread light mayo or cream cheese on a sandwich instead of butter and cut calories by half.

9. Check the label of your vegetable oil and select safflower, corn, sunflower, soybean, olive or canola.

10. Buy nonstick vegetable sprays to use in place of butter or oil on pans and baking sheets.

Citrus Chicken Breasts

Ingredients

3 medium chicken breasts, split and skinned

¼ tsp. finely shredded orange peel
½ cup orange juice
1 Tbsp. sliced green onion
2 tsp. instant chicken bouillon granules

1 Tbsp. cornstarch
½ tsp. paprika
1 Tbsp. cold water
Dash of salt and pepper

Yield: 6 servings

Directions

Place chicken in 12" x 7" x 2" baking dish.

Combine orange peel, juice, onion, and bouillon granules. Sprinkle chicken with a little salt, pepper, and paprika; pour orange juice mixture over. Cover and bake in 375° oven for 45 minutes or till chicken is done. Remove chicken; keep warm. Measure pan juices. Add water, if necessary, to measure ¾ cup liquid.

In saucepan, combine cornstarch, paprika and cold water; stir in pan juices. Cook and stir till mixture thickens and bubbles. Heat through. Spoon some sauce over chicken; save excess for extra sauce. Garnish with orange slices, if desired. Serve and decorate with wild rice.

This recipe submitted by Gale Larabee

MEAT & FISH

Cal 160   Fat 2.3 g

Cranberry-Orange Chicken

Ingredients

2½ to 3-pound broiler-fryer, cut up and skin removed
1 10½ oz. can condensed beef broth
¾ cup cranberry juice cocktail

2 medium oranges, thinly sliced

1 Tbsp. cornstarch
1 Tbsp. water
Dash of salt

Yield: 4 servings

Directions

In medium saucepan, combine chicken neck, giblets, and beef broth. Simmer, covered for 1 hour; strain broth. Add cranberry juice cocktail to broth; boil, uncovered, till liquid is reduced to 1 cup.

Meanwhile place chicken in a 12" x 8" x 2" baking dish. Season with salt. Bake in 350° oven for 25 minutes. Add orange slices to chicken pieces; bake 30 to 35 minutes more.

To serve, blend cornstarch with the 1 tablespoon water; stir into broth. Cook and stir till sauce thickens and bubbles. Drizzle sauce over chicken.

This recipe submitted by Gale Larabee

Cal 226   Fat 4.3

M E A T & F I S H

Szechuan Orange-Ginger Chicken

This popular recipe is much easier and faster to make than it looks. Chinese dishes from the Szechuan region usually have a spicy, hot flavour; if you prefer it milder, use less chili paste – the dish is delicious either way.

Ingredients

4 chicken breasts, skinned and boned (about 1 lb. boneless)
1 sweet green pepper
1 sweet red pepper

1 orange

1 tsp. bottled chili paste
2 Tbsp. sherry
1 tsp. granulated sugar
1 tsp. cornstarch

1 tsp. Mirin (Japanese seasoning)
1 Tbsp. vegetable oil
1 tsp. minced garlic
1 Tbsp. minced fresh gingerroot

Yield: 4 servings

Directions

Cut chicken into 1-inch squares; set aside. Halve green and red peppers and remove ribs and seeds; cut into 1-inch squares.

Using vegetable peeler, remove rind from orange (orange part only, no white). Cut rind into thin julienne strips about 1½ inches long; set aside. Squeeze orange and reserve ¼ cup juice.

In small bowl, combine reserved orange juice, chili paste, sherry, sugar, and cornstarch; stir until smooth.

In wok, heat oil over high heat; add seasoning and chicken and stir-fry for 2 minutes or until no longer pink. Remove chicken. Add orange rind, garlic and gingerroot; stir-fry for 10 seconds. Add peppers and stir-fry for 1 minute. Add chili paste mixture and bring to a boil. Return chicken to wok and stir until heated through. Serve with rice.

MEAT & FISH

Cal 220   Fat 10 g

Oriental Chicken

Oriental cooking without the wok!

Ingredients

1 large sweet red pepper, cored, seeded and cut into thin slices
¼ pound snow peas, cleaned and strings removed
½ cup water chestnuts, sliced
⅓ cup chopped green onion
4 boneless, skinned chicken breast halves (6 ounces each)

3 Tbsp. low-sodium soy sauce
1 Tbsp. sesame oil
½ tsp. grated, peeled fresh gingerroot
1 clove garlic, finely chopped

Yield: 4 servings

Directions

Preheat oven to very hot (500°). Tear off four 14" x 12" sheets of regular-weight aluminum foil. Lightly oil center of lower half of each sheet with vegetable oil. Place one-eight of the red pepper, snow peas, water chestnuts and green onion on oiled portion of each foil sheet. Place a chicken breast on vegetables. Sprinkle remaining vegetables over chicken.

Stir together soy sauce, sesame oil, gingerroot and garlic in small bowl. Spoon the mixture evenly over the chicken and vegetables. Fold upper half of foil over ingredients, matching up edges evenly and enclose filling. Fold to make a completely sealed packet. Place 2 cookie sheets in the preheated oven for about 2 minutes.

CONTINUED NEXT PAGE

MEAT & FISH

Cal 459   Fat 7.2 g

Place the aluminum foil packets in a single layer on the hot cookie sheets. Bake packets in very hot oven (500°) for 12 minutes. Carefully fold back edges of packet and serve immediately with rice or whole wheat noodles.

Southern Fried Chicken Strips

For those once in a while fried-food cravings, this recipe is quite reasonable in fat content.

Ingredients

¼ cup 1 % milk
½ cup plain low-fat yogurt

1 pound boneless, skinned
  chicken breasts, cut into strips
  about 3" x ½" x ½"

¾ cup all-purpose flour
¾ tsp. leaf thyme, crumbled
½ tsp. salt substitute
½ tsp. black pepper
¼ tsp. ground hot red pepper

Vegetable oil for frying

Yield: 4 servings

Directions

Combine milk and yogurt in medium-size bowl.

Add chicken strips; toss to mix well.

Combine flour, thyme, salt, black pepper and red pepper on a piece of wax paper; stir to mix.

Pour about ¼" oil into cast-iron skillet. Heat over medium-high heat.

Remove chicken pieces from the yogurt mixture, thinly but evenly coated. Toss the chicken, a few pieces at a time, into the flour mixture. When oil is hot (about 325°), add coated strips. Work in batches and do not crowd pieces, letting the oil heat up before adding the second batch. Fry chicken until brown on bottom; then turn to brown other side. Remove with slotted spoon; drain well on paper towelling. Serve immediately.

M E A T & F I S H

Cal 300   Fat 9 g

Peppery Chicken Stir-Fry

Ingredients

1 lb. boneless chicken breasts,
   cut in strips
2 Tbsp. low-sodium soy sauce

1 Tbsp. oil (sesame)
1 tsp. Mirin (Japanese seasoning
6 green onions, thinly sliced
2 cloves garlic, crushed
1 Tbsp. chopped fresh gingerroot

1 each of green and red sweet
   peppers, sliced

1 Tbsp. cornstarch
½ cup chicken stock or water
¼–½ tsp. dried red pepper
   flakes

Yield: 4 servings

Directions

Toss chicken strips in soy sauce
and marinate 1 hour.

Heat wok or heavy skillet to
medium/high heat. Add 1 tablespoon of oil, stir-fry chicken with
marinate 3-4 minutes or until
chicken is opaque. Remove and
set aside.

Add remaining oil to wok; add
flavouring, onions, garlic and
ginger, stir-fry 2 minutes.

Add vegetables, stir-fry 2 minutes.

Mix cornstarch, stock and pepper flakes in bowl. Return
chicken to wok; and add stock
mixture. Bring to a boil and simmer until sauce thickens, about
1 minute. Serve on a bed of rice
or whole wheat noodles.

MEAT & FISH

Cal 285   Fat 11.4 g

Chicken Chili

Ingredients

1 lb. ground chicken
1 medium onion, chopped
1 medium green pepper, chopped
1 large garlic clove, chopped

2½ cups kidney beans
2½ cups canned tomatoes
½ Tbsp. chili powder
½ tsp. black pepper
½ tsp. paprika
1 ½ tsp. salt (optional)

Directions

Brown ground chicken in non-stick pan, add chopped onion, green pepper and garlic, stir to combine. Simmer until onion and pepper are soft.

Add kidney beans, canned tomatoes and spices, stir to combine (may transfer to slow cooker or pot). Simmer for 1 hour or longer. If too dry, add more tomatoes.

Yield: 6 to 8 servings

This recipe submitted by Valerie Morris.

Cal 258

Fat 2.7 g

M E A T & F I S H

Orange Chicken Oriental

Ingredients

4 chicken legs with thighs
   attached

¾ cup chicken broth
¾ cup orange juice
1 ½ Tbsp. low-sodium soy sauce
1 ½ Tbsp. ketchup
1 large garlic clove, crushed
1 tsp. sesame oil

1 orange

Optional: parsley, finely
chopped

Yield: 4 servings

Directions

Skin chicken legs and set aside
until ready to use.

In a large wide saucepan, bring
remaining ingredients, except
orange and parsley, to a boil.
Add skinned chicken legs. Then
cover and simmer gently over
low heat until chicken is cooked,
about 25 to 30 minutes. Turn
chicken halfway through cooking.

While chicken is cooking, peel
orange and split into sections.
Once chicken is cooked, remove
to a platter and cover to keep
warm. Vigorously boil remaining
liquid, uncovered, until reduced
by half, about 5 minutes. Place
a piece of chicken on each dinner plate. Top each with a few
orange sections. Then spoon 1
or 2 tablespoons sauce over
top. Sprinkle with parsley, if you
wish.

MEAT & FISH

Cal 259   Fat 11.7 g

Tandoori Chicken

Ingredients

2 Tbsp. low-fat yogurt
1 tsp. olive oil
2 tsp. each of curry powder and
  ground cumin
Generous pinches of ground ginger and cayenne pepper
4 chicken breasts, skinned and
  boned

Directions

Preheat broiler. In a small bowl, stir yogurt with oil, curry powder, cumin, ginger and cayenne until well combined. Place chicken on a rack set in a shallow baking dish. Brush top of chicken breasts with half the yogurt mixture. Place pan containing chicken on an oven rack about 6 inches away from broiler. Broil for 3 minutes. Then turn chicken breasts and brush with remaining yogurt mixture. Then continue to broil for 3 to 4 more minutes or until chicken springs back when lightly touched. Serve chicken with steamed rice and a cucumber salad.

MEAT & FISH

Yield: 4 servings

Cal 177   Fat 10 g

Chicken Greek-Style

Ingredients

¾ cup chicken broth
2 Tbsp. lemon juice
2-8 oz. chicken breasts, skinned
1 tsp. olive oil
Dash each of garlic powder and
 white pepper
½ tsp. each oregano leaves and
 salt

Directions

Preheat oven to 350°. Pour broth and lemon juice into small baking pan. Rub chicken breasts with 1 teaspoon oil and place in pan. Sprinkle with seasonings and bake 20 minutes.

MEAT & FISH

Yield: 4 servings

Cal 238   Fat 9 g

Orange-Mustard Chicken

M
E
A
T
&
F
I
S
H

Ingredients

1 Tsp. olive oil
4 chicken breasts, skinned and
   boned

½ cup orange juice
2 tsp. Dijon mustard
½ tsp. leaf thyme & sage
Freshly ground black pepper

Yield: 4 servings

Directions

Heat oil in a large non-stick frying pan over medium-high heat. Add chicken and saute just until golden, about 2 minutes per side.

Meanwhile, whisk orange juice with remaining ingredients. When chicken is golden, add orange juice mixture to frying pan. Cover and reduce heat to low. Simmer gently for 3 to 4 minutes per side, stirring juice mixture occasionally, just until chicken feels springy to the touch. Remove chicken to a platter. Increase heat to high. Boil orange juice mixture vigorously until reduced to a saucelike consistency, about 2 minutes. Spoon over chicken. Serve immediately.

Cal 188   Fat 9 g

Spicy Baked Chicken

Ingredients

¼ cup whole wheat flour
2 Tbsp. snipped parsley
1 Tbsp. low-calorie Italian salad
   dressing mix
2 tsp. diet margarine, softened
½ tsp. paprika

3 Tbsp. water

1-3 lb. broiler-fryer chicken, cut
   up

Directions

In small bowl stir together flour, parsley, salad dressing mix, margarine and paprika.

Blend in water.

Remove wing tips and skin from chicken. Spread flour mixture over skinned chicken pieces. Place chicken in ungreased 15" x 10" x 1" baking pan. bake in 375° oven for 50 to 60 minutes. Do not turn.

MEAT & FISH

Yield: 6 servings

Cal 193   Fat 9.3 g

Chicken Paprikash

Ingredients

¼ cup chopped onion
¼ cup chopped green pepper
1 tsp. sesame seed oil

4½ tsp. Hungarian-style paprika
½ tsp. dried marjoram, crushed

2 chicken breasts, split and skin
removed

¾ cup chicken broth
1 ounce Neufchâtel cheese
1 Tbsp. low-fat plain yogurt
1 tsp. arrowroot

Accent
2 Tbsp. snipped parsley

Yield: 4 servings

Directions

In heavy oven-going skillet cook onion and green pepper in hot oil till tender but not brown.

Sprinkle with 3 tsp. of the paprika and the marjoram; stir to combine. Top with the chicken breasts; sprinkle with remaining paprika. Cover and bake in 350° oven for 35 to 40 minutes or till done.

Add chicken broth; simmer on range top 2 to 3 minutes. Remove chicken breasts; keep warm. Pour contents of skillet into blender; add cheese, yogurt and arrowroot and blend till smooth. Return chicken breasts to skillet; spoon sauce over chicken. Simmer, uncovered, for 5 minutes. Season to taste with Mrs. Dash. Sprinkle with parsley. Serve with rice.

MEAT & FISH

Cal 185   Fat 11 g

Goulash (Turkey) Viennese

Ingredients

2 cups onion, chopped

½ lb. mushrooms, sliced
2 garlic cloves, chopped
½ tsp. marjoram
1-2 lbs. turkey breast, cubed
1 tsp. caraway seeds
½ tsp. salt (optional)

½ cup warm water with 2 beef
    bouillon cubes dissolved
2 Tbsp. Hungarian paprika

Directions

Sauté onions in non-stick pan (add 1 Tbsp. water if necessary).

Add the remaining ingredients, except the beef broth and paprika and sauté until meat is tender.

When meat is tender add the beef broth and paprika. Mix well and serve on brown rice or whole wheat noodles.

MEAT & FISH

Yield: 6 servings

This recipe was submitted by Valerie Morris.

Cal 206

Fat 2.9 g

Westerner's Chili

MEAT & FISH

Ingredients

1 cup chopped green bell
   pepper
1¼ cups chopped onion
2 cloves fresh garlic, minced
1 Tbsp. oil

1 can (28 oz.) kidney beans,
   drained
1 can (28 oz.) stewed tomatoes
1 cup water
2 cups cubed cooked turkey
1 Tbsp. chili powder
1 tsp. dried coriander
1 tsp. crushed red pepper
Chopped onion or chopped
   cilantro for garnish

Directions

Sauté green pepper, onion, and
garlic in oil until soft.

Add beans, tomatoes, water,
turkey and seasonings. Simmer
25 minutes. Garnish, if desired.

Yield: 6 servings

Cal 296   Fat 5.8 g

Turkey Broccoli Bake

Ingredients

4 cups sliced broccoli (diagonally ¼ inch)
½ cup onions, sliced in rings
1 package chicken broth

1 tsp. + 1 Tbsp. margarine
1 tsp. + 1 Tbsp. cornstarch

⅔ cup nonfat dry milk (powder)
1 tsp. sherry extract
Dash of salt & pepper

1 lb. cooked turkey, sliced
Dash paprika

Yield: 4 servings

Directions

In a saucepan cook broccoli and onion 5 minutes. Drain liquid into a 2 cup measure and set veggies aside. Add enough water to veggie liquid to make 2 cups liquid, add packet of broth mix.

In the top of a double boiler set over simmering water, melt margarine, add cornstarch and blend into a paste. Add veggie liquid, stirring constantly.

Slowly blend in nonfat dry milk and cook slowly stirring until thickened about 20 minutes. Add sherry extract, salt and pepper.

Spray 2-quart casserole dish with non-stick cooking spray. Place turkey slices in centre of dish and arrange broccoli and onion slices around turkey, top with sauce. Sprinkle salt and paprika over sauce. Cover and bake at 350° for 30 minutes.

MEAT & FISH

Cal 267   Fat 7 g

Country-Style Turkey

Ingredients

1 half turkey breast, about 3
    pounds
1 Tbsp. oil
½ tsp. salt
¼ tsp. pepper
¼ tsp. marjoram

1 lb. carrots, peeled, halved
1 lb. russet potatoes
½ lb. small onions, peeled
1½ lb. cabbage, cut into wedges

Tangy Glaze Sauce:
⅓ cup ketchup
3 Tbsp. cider vinegar
2 Tbsp. honey
1 Tbsp. prepared mustard.

Directions

Brush turkey with oil; sprinkle
with seasonings. Roast 1 hour at
350°, basting occasionally with
drippings.

Prepare Tangy Glaze

In large saucepan, cook carrots,
potatoes and onions in simmering water 8 minutes. Add
cabbage wedges; simmer 5 minutes, drain. Brush turkey with
glaze; surround with vegetables.
Continue roasting 45 minutes,
basting turkey with glaze and
vegetables with drippings until
turkey registers 170° and juices
are clear.

MEAT & FISH

Yield: 6 servings

Cal 276   Fat 11.5 g

Peppery Turkey Slices

Ingredients

1 ¼ lbs. turkey breast slices
1 clove fresh garlic, minced
1 Tbsp. margarine

¾ cup dry white wine
1 Tbsp. Dijon-style mustard
3 green onions, minced
½ cup mushrooms, sliced
3 Tbsp. green peppercorns
Salt and pepper

Directions

Sauté turkey slices and garlic in margarine about 2 minutes, turning once. Reserve turkey slices; keep warm.

Combine remaining ingredients to juices in pan and simmer together until slightly thickened, about 20 minutes. Serve over turkey.

Yield: 6 servings

M E A T & F I S H

Cal 210   Fat 2 g

Turkey Cutlets

Ingredients

1 ½ pounds turkey breast, sliced
    into cutlets
1 egg, beaten
¼ cup 1 % milk
½ cup ground almonds
½ cup seasoned whole wheat
    bread crumbs
1 Tbsp. margarine and non-stick
    spray
Lemon juice (optional)

Directions

Pound turkey cutlets until flat
and thin. Dip in combined egg
and milk and then into mixed
almonds and bread crumbs.
Sauté over medium-high heat in
oil and margarine until golden
brown on each side; transfer to
warm platter. Sprinkle with
lemon juice if desired.

Yield: 4 servings

Cal 273   Fat 9.7 g

Turkey Pasta Salad

Ingredients

1 Tbsp. olive oil
1 clove fresh garlic, minced
2 green onions, chopped
½ lb. broccoli, cut in florets
2 zucchini, sliced

¼ lb. snow peas
1 carrot, julienned
1 cup chopped, cooked turkey
2 Tbsp. each fresh parsley &
  basil, chopped, or ½ tsp. each
  dried

8 oz. hot, cooked whole wheat
  pasta (corkscrews, bow-ties)
¼ cup half and half cream
Salt and pepper
1 Tbsp. grated parmesan

Directions

In hot oil, sauté garlic, onions, broccoli and zucchini for 3 minutes. Add ¼ cup water; cover and steam 4 minutes.

Stir in snow peas, carrot, turkey, parsley and basil. Cook, stirring until hot.

Add cooked pasta and toss. Stir in half and half, seasonings, and cheese.

MEAT & FISH

Yield: 4 servings

Cal 446   Fat 9.4 g

Citrus Turkey with Rice

MICROWAVEABLE

M
E
A
T
&
F
I
S
H

Ingredients

2 cups cubed turkey
1 clove garlic, minced

1 Tbsp. margarine
1 cup long grain rice
½ cup diced onion

2 Tbsp. orange zest
½ cup toasted slivered almonds
⅓ cup (plumped) raisins
1 Tbsp. grated fresh ginger
¼ tsp. salt

Water
½ cup orange juice
¼ cup lemon juice

Yield: 6 servings

Directions

Cook turkey with garlic in covered microwaveable container 2-4 minutes on High. Reserve juice.

Combine margarine, rice and onion in large casserole. Microwave on High 2 minutes. Stir.

Mix in orange zest, almonds, raisins, ginger, salt.

Combine turkey stock and water to make 1¼ cups. Pour over rice with orange and lemon juice. Cover and cook on High 5-6 minutes then on Med-High 11-14 minutes till rice is tender. Stir and let stand 6 minutes.

Meat Variations: Beef or pork, cubed. Microwave on medium and use 2-3 tablespoons grated fresh ginger.

This recipe submitted by Gale Larabee

Cal 70   Fat 6.9 g

Spicy Lamb Chili

Ingredients

3 Tbsp. vegetable oil
3 lb. boneless lamb leg or shoulder, or stewing beef, trimmed of fat and cut into ½ inch cubes

2 onions, sliced and cut into 1 inch pieces
2 green peppers, sliced and cut into 1 inch pieces
6 cloves garlic, crushed
3 Tbsp. all-purpose flour
3 to 4 Tbsp. chili powder
1 Tbsp. each of ground cumin, thyme and coriander
1 tsp. dried leaf oregano
½ tsp. cinnamon
Dash of salt substitute

28-oz. can diced tomatoes with juice
3½ oz. can jalapeno peppers, seeded and drained, or ¼ cup finely chopped fresh hot peppers
2 cups beef bouillon or broth
19-oz. can white kidney beans, drained and rinsed

19-oz. can red kidney beans, drained and rinsed

Yield: 12 cups

Directions

Heat 1 tablespoon vegetable oil in a large saucepan over medium heat. Cook lamb cubes in hot pan, turning frequently, until evenly browned. Remove from pan and set aside. Reduce heat to medium-low.

Add remaining tablespoon of oil to pan, cook onions, green peppers and garlic for 5 minutes stirring often. Sprinkle with flour and seasonings. Continue stirring until vegetables are aromatic, about 2 more minutes.

Stir in diced tomatoes with juice, peppers and browned lamb. Add beef bouillon. Cover and bring to a boil. Reduce heat and simmer gently, covered, for about

CONTINUED NEXT PAGE

MEAT & FISH

Cal 278   Fat 8 g

M
E
A
T
&
F
I
S
H

1 ½ to 2 hours, until meat is very tender. Stir often.

Stir drained and rinsed beans into the chili and simmer for 2 to 3 minutes, until hot.

Optional: Serve chili topped with grated low-fat cheddar or Monterey Jack cheese and chopped green onion.

Refrigerated, chili will keep well for at least 2 days. It also freezes well.

Glazed Orange Pork

Ingredients

¼ cup orange juice
2 Tbsp. ginger marmalade
Generous grinding of black
  pepper
Pinch of cinnamon

1 lb. pork tenderloin

Directions

Preheat oven to 350°. In a small bowl, whisk orange juice with ginger marmalade, black pepper and pinch of cinnamon. Remove any large pieces of peel from marmalade, finely chop and add. Mixture will be used for basting pork tenderloin.

Trim any excess fat from pork tenderloin. Then place in a roasting pan just large enough to hold it snugly. Bake in centre of preheated oven for 35 to 40 minutes, basting frequently with orange juice mixture, until pork tenderloin is cooked through and glazed.

MEAT & FISH

Yield: 4 servings

Cal 173   Fat 4.4 g

Pork à l'Orange

Ingredients

2 pork tenderloins, about ¾ lb. each

⅓ cup orange juice
1 Tbsp. Dijon mustard
½ tsp. rosemary, crumbled
¼ tsp. leaf thyme
Generous grinding of black pepper

Directions

Preheat oven to 375°. Place 2 tenderloins in a small ovenproof dish just large enough to hold them.

Whisk remaining ingredients together. Pour over top. Bake, uncovered, for 30 to 40 minutes, basting often and turning halfway through cooking.

Yield: 6 servings

Cal 141   Fat 3.1 g

Sliced Steak Sandwich

Ingredients

1 ½ pounds lean round tip steak
(fat trimmed)

¼ cup chopped scallions
1 Tbsp. olive oil
1 Tbsp. low-sodium soy sauce
2 Tbsp. lemon juice
½ tsp. thyme
¼ tsp. rosemary

6 slices whole wheat toast

Yield: 6 servings

Directions

Score round steak on both sides
with a sharp knife.

Combine scallions, oil, soy
sauce, lemon juice, thyme and
rosemary in a baking dish large
enough to hold the round steak.
Place steak in marinade. Turn to
coat top. Cover and marinate in
the refrigerator, 1 hour. If
desired, pierce steak with a fork
to tenderize. Broil the steak 8 to
11 minutes on each side, or until
cooked to desired degree.
Transfer to a cutting board and
keeping the knife almost horizontal, thinly slice the meat
across the grain. Reserve the
juice.

Place a slice of toast on each
serving plate. Place steak on
top. Spoon the juice over meat.

MEAT & FISH

Cal 267   Fat 8.3 g

Swiss Steak

Ingredients

2 lbs. round steak (fat trimmed)
4 Tbsp. flour

Non-stick cooking spray
1 large onion, chopped
1 cup celery

1 8-oz. can low-sodium tomato
   sauce
1 cup water
3 Tbsp. grated carrot
1 tsp. leaf marjoram (crumbled)
¼ tsp. pepper

Directions

Rub steak with flour to coat generously, brown in a large heavy frying pan coated with non-stick cooking spray. Remove and set aside for next step.

Sauté onions and celery until soft.

In same frying pan stir in remaining ingredients. Return steak to pan, cover, and simmer 2 hours or until meat is very tender. Remove to a heated platter.

Yield: 6 servings

Cal 279   Fat 9.1 g

Oriental Tuna Stir-Fry

Ingredients

¾ pound tuna steak, skin and
  dark meat removed
3 Tbsp. cornstarch

2 tsp. peanut oil
16 snow peas
1 small carrot, sliced diagonally
  into ¼-inch strips
1 2-inch piece white radish, split
  lengthwise, sliced into ¼-inch
  slices
4 cups sliced bok choy or
  Chinese cabbage
½ cup fresh bean sprouts

½ cup chicken stock
½ tsp. sesame oil
1 tsp. low-sodium soy sauce
1 tsp. toasted sesame seeds

Yield: 4 servings

Directions

Toss fish with cornstarch to coat
evenly. Set aside.

Heat 1 teaspoon peanut oil in a
wok or large nonstick skillet,
medium-high, 1 minute. Add
peas, carrot, radish, bok choy or
Chinese cabbage, and sprouts
and stir-fry, 2 minutes. Remove
from wok or skillet; set aside.

Add remaining peanut oil to the
wok. Toss in fish and stir-fry,
about 3 minutes. Return vegetables to the wok and toss with
fish. Add chicken stock, sesame
oil, and soy sauce. Bring to a
boil, stir and remove from heat.
Sprinkle with sesame seeds and
serve.

MEAT & FISH

Cal 227   Fat 6.5 g

Fish Portuguese

Ingredients

20-oz. can tomatoes
½ cup red or white wine
1 Tbsp. drained capers
1 large garlic clove, crushed
3 Tbsp. grated carrot
½ tsp. oregano and basil

4 fish steaks or fillets, such as
    cod or halibut

Directions

Combine all ingredients, except fish steaks, in a large wide frying pan with deep sides. Break up tomatoes. Bring to a boil. Add fish. Cover and reduce heat to low. Simmer, stirring often, for 5 minutes. Turn fish and simmer for 5 more minutes. Remove fish to a platter. Increase heat to high. Boil tomato mixture, uncovered, stirring constantly, until thickened. Pour over fish and serve with rice.

M E A T & F I S H

Yield: 4 servings

Cal 179

Fat 7 g

Sole Florentine

Ingredients

- 1 pound fresh or frozen sole fillets or other fish fillets
- 1 10-oz. package frozen leaf spinach

- 1 medium onion, sliced and separated into rings
- ¼ tsp. salt
- 4 whole black peppercorns

- ½ cup chicken broth
- 2 Tbsp. dry white wine

- ½ cup evaporated skim milk
- 1 Tbsp. all-purpose flour
- ½ tsp. dried dillweed
- ¼ tsp. dried oregano, crushed

Yield: 4 servings

Directions

Thaw fish, if frozen. Cook spinach according to package directions; drain well. Set aside and keep warm.

Meanwhile, in skillet layer fish fillets and onion rings. Sprinkle with salt; add peppercorns.

Add chicken broth and wine; bring to boiling. Reduce heat. Cover skillet and simmer for 7 to 8 minutes or till fish flakes easily with a fork. Remove fish; keep warm.

Meanwhile, for sauce, combine evaporated milk, flour, dillweed, and oregano; stir till smooth. Stir into mixture in skillet. Cook, stirring gently, over medium heat till thickened and bubbly. Cook and stir 1 to 2 minutes more. Remove peppercorns. Serve fish and sauce over cooked spinach. Garnish with lemon peel curls and fresh dillweed, if desired.

MEAT & FISH

Cal 139   Fat 1.8 g

Poached Fish with Dill Sauce

Ingredients

3 lbs. fresh or previously frozen
   dressed fish
2 cups water
3 lemon slices
1 bay leaf
1 tsp. seasoning salt
¼ tsp. dried tarragon, crushed

2 Tbsp. diet margarine
4 tsp. all-purpose flour
2 tsp. lemon juice
½ tsp. sugar
½ tsp. dried dillweed
1 beaten egg yolk

Yield: 8 servings

Directions

Place fish on large piece of
cheesecloth; fold cloth over fish.
Place on rack in poaching pan.
Add water, lemon slices, bay
leaf, salt, and tarragon. Cover
and simmer 25 to 30 minutes or
till fish flakes easily when tested
with a fork. Remove from pan;
keep warm. Strain and reserve 1
cup cooking liquid.

For sauce, in saucepan melt
margarine; stir in flour. Add
reserved liquid, lemon juice,
sugar, and dillweed. Cook and
stir till thickened and bubbly.
Gradually stir ½ cup of hot mixture into egg yolk; return to hot
mixture. Cook and stir 1 to 2
minutes more. Keep warm.

Pull foil and cloth away from
fish; remove and discard skin.
Transfer fish to platter using 2
spatulas. Top with some sauce;
put leftover sauce in a server for
extras on the side.

Cal 100   Fat 3.6 g

Baked Red Snapper

Ingredients

2 lbs. fresh or previously frozen
   red snapper fillets or other
   fish fillets
2 Tbsp. lemon juice
¼ tsp. of cloves and mace

½ cup chopped celery
½ cup chopped onion
¼ cup chopped green pepper

¾ cup vegetable juice cocktail

Directions

Place fillets in greased baking pan. Drizzle juice over fish. Sprinkle with ¼ teaspoons of cloves and mace. Bake fish in 350° oven for 10 minutes.

Meanwhile, prepare sauce. In saucepan combine celery, onion, green pepper and vegetable juice cocktail. Simmer, uncovered, for 10 minutes.

Remove fish from oven. Drain off liquid. Pour vegetable sauce over fish. Return fish to oven and bake 15 minutes more or till fish flakes easily when tested with a fork, basting with the vegetable sauce occasionally.

MEAT & FISH

Yield: 6 servings

Cal 162   Fat 2 g

Shrimp Newberg

Though this recipe is relatively low in fat, the egg yolks and shrimp may be a consideration to anyone with high cholesterol.

Ingredients

6 ounces fresh or frozen shelled shrimp, halved lengthwise
1 Tbsp. diet margarine
5 tsp. cornstarch
¼ tsp. salt substitute
1¼ cups skim milk
2 beaten egg yolks
2 Tbsp. sherry extract
2 tsp. lemon juice
3 toasted English muffin halves
Paprika

Directions

Thaw shrimp, if frozen. In saucepan melt margarine; stir in cornstarch and salt. Add milk all at once. Cook and stir till bubbly; cook and stir 2 minutes more. Stir half the hot mixture into egg yolks. Return to hot mixture. Cook and stir till bubbly. Add shrimp; cook and stir till shrimp is cooked. Stir in sherry and lemon juice. Spoon over muffin halves. Sprinkle with paprika.

Yield: 3 servings

Cal 242   Fat 7.6 g

Crustless Crabmeat & Vegetable Pie

M I C R O W A V E A B L E

Ingredients

- 1 cup each sliced zucchini and mushrooms
- 8 egg whites, slightly beaten
- 1 cup evaporated skim milk
- 1 tsp. Dijon mustard
- ¼ tsp. turmeric
- 1 8-oz. package frozen imitation crab, thawed or fresh
- ½ cup low-fat swiss cheese, shredded
- 2 Tbsp. minced chives
- Dash cayenne pepper

Directions

Combine all above ingredients in a 1-quart micro-proof dish. Microwave uncovered for 3 minutes on High power, until crisp and tender.

MEAT & FISH

Yield: 4 servings

Cal 287   Fat 5.5 g

Ribbon Skewered Halibut
MICROWAVEABLE

MEAT & FISH

Ingredients

1 pound halibut steaks, cut into
  1-2 inch cubes
Juice of 1 lemon
Juice of 1 lime
1 tsp. parsley

1 yellow pepper, cut into 1-inch
  square pieces
1 red pepper, cut into 1-inch
  square pieces
1 green pepper, cut into 1-inch
  square pieces
1 zucchini, sliced and cut into
  quarters
14 mushrooms

Directions

Combine juice and parsley and marinate halibut.

Arrange halibut on wooden skewers alternating with squares of red, yellow and green peppers, zucchini and mushroom. Place on a microwaveable plate and cook on High power (saran wrapped), 4 minutes for 7 kabobs. Repeat with remaining kabobs. Serve kabobs over brown rice.

Yield: 7 servings

This recipe submitted by Gale Larabee.

Cal 198   Fat 2 g

Halibut Italian-Style

MICROWAVEABLE

Ingredients

4 halibut steaks, about 6 oz. each

¼ cup white wine

1 Tbsp. freshly squeezed lemon juice

½ tsp. oregano

¼ cup finely chopped fresh basil

¼ cup finely chopped fresh parsley

¼ cup finely chopped red pepper

Yield: 4 servings

Oven directions

Preheat oven to 450°. Arrange halibut steaks in an oven dish large enough to hold them snugly. In a small bowl, whisk wine with lemon juice and oregano. Pour mixture over fish both sides. Top with basil, parsley and red pepper. Bake, uncovered, in preheated oven for 10 to 12 minutes or until flaky. Baste with wine mixture several times during baking.

Microwave Directions

Arrange halibut in a dish with thick pieces toward outside edge of dish. In a small bowl, whisk wine with lemon juice and italian seasoning. Pour over fish both sides. Microwave, covered, on high for 3 minutes. Turn fish. Top with basil, parsley and red pepper. Continue to microwave, covered, on high for 3 to 4 more minutes until flaky. Let stand for 2 minutes.

MEAT & FISH

Cal 534

Fat 1 g

Desserts

Low-Fat Choices

Instead Of	You Could Choose
1 raisin bran muffin...	1 raisin bagel or whole wheat bagel
1 blueberry muffin...	1 blueberry bagel
1 oz. roaster peanuts...	10 oz. roasted chestnuts
1 oz. potato chips...	10 oz. pretzels
¼ cup chocolate chips...	1 cup jelly beans
1 small chocolate chip cookie...	4 fig bars
1 small brownie...	6 graham crackers
½ cup vanilla ice cream...	cone of frozen yogurt
Cheezies, Cracker Jacks...	fluffy pop corn
1 apple turnover...	1 large juicy fresh apple, baked with cinnamon, raisins and a sprinkle of water over it.

Jelly Beans and Gummy Bears

Both of these types of candy are fat free and very low in sodium, but 100 percent of their calories comes from refined sugar. They contain no fiber, no vitamins, and virtually no minerals. This is the way to go if you want sugar-based junk food with no fat.

Raisins and Dried Fruits

Raisins are the "health food" counterpart to jelly beans. Although they get most of their calories from sugar, raisins do contain some fiber, vitamins and minerals. They are just as likely to cause tooth decay as jelly beans, however, because they stick to your teeth.

Dessert Fat Tips

1. Breakfast treats like doughnuts and croissants lack staying power. They are empty fat calories and will leave you tired and feeling sluggish by 10:00 or 11:00. Try multi-grain bagels with jam or hot oatmeal sweetened with raisins and cinnamon instead.

2. In the morning, choose dry toast over a croissant or muffin. A small croissant rings in at 5.6 grams of fat, a large muffin at 7.8 grams, while toast is 0.7 grams.

3. There are some commercially prepared cookies low in fat - Newton-type cookies and gingersnaps. Plain angel food cake has no fat. Two grams of fat or less per portion is best.

4. Many so called health chips and rice crackers are high in saturated fatty acids. However, some are cooked in unsaturated oil. The best are those labelled as having more polyunsaturated than saturated fats.

5. Sweeten plain low-fat or non-fat yogurt with puréed fruit or applesauce or artificial sweetener if you like it with your fruit or a little bit of vanilla extract or any of your favourite extract – lemon, chocolate, maple, etc.

Graham Bread

Ingredients

2 Tbsp. brown sugar
1 Tsp. baking powder
½ tsp. baking soda
1 cup all-purpose flour
2 cups graham flour
½ tsp. salt
½ cup soaked raisins (optional)

1¾ cups skim milk

Directions

Combine all ingredients except milk, stirring to blend well.

Add milk. Stir just to mix. Pour into a large margarine-greased Crisco container. Seal the top of the tin with greased aluminum foil. Bake in moderate oven, 350° for 1½ hours. Do not peek! Remove from can immediately when done. Cool and wrap in foil. Freeze, if desired, in plastic bag. Slice thin when serving.

This recipes was submitted by Donna Graham.

Calories and fat per 4 oz. serving:

Yield: 5 lb. loaf

DESSERTS

Cal 122

Fat 0.4 g

Buttermilk Fruit Bread

Ingredients

1 ¼ cups all-purpose sifted flour
1 cup whole wheat flour
2 tsp. baking powder
1 tsp. salt
½ tsp. baking soda
1 cup chopped fruit or nuts
2 eggs, beaten well

⅔ cup honey
2 Tbsp. melted light margarine
1 cup buttermilk *

* An alternative to buttermilk is to substitute normal milk with 1 tablespoon of vinegar or lemon juice. Let stand for 5 minutes.

Yield: 1 loaf

Directions

Grease bottom of 9" x 5" x 3" loaf pan. Line with wax paper, then grease paper. Sift together dry ingredients, add fruit or nuts. Add well beaten eggs.

Mix honey, melted margarine and buttermilk and fold into dry mix, blending only until well mixed. Bake in 325° oven for 55 minutes or until bread is done in centre. Cool 10 minutes before removing from pan. For better flavour and easy cutting, cool bread overnight. Try apples, raisins, walnuts. Add cinnamon, cloves and nutmeg to your taste!

This recipe submitted by Gale Larabee.

Calories and fat per 4 oz. serving:

DESSERTS

Cranberry Bran Muffins

Ingredients

1 ½ cups bran
½ cup boiling water

1 egg
½ cup honey
8 oz. low-fat yogurt
¼ cup oil

1 ¼ cups whole wheat flour
1 ¼ tsp. baking soda
¼ tsp. salt

½ cup chopped cranberries

Variation: ¼ cup currants or raisins

Directions

Preheat oven to 375°. Combine bran and water; let stand 10 minutes.

Add egg, honey, yogurt and oil to bran and blend well.

Combine flour, soda and salt; add to batter.

Stir in cranberries. Fill muffin tins lined with paper baking cups. Bake 15 to 20 minutes. Remove muffins from pan and cool for at least 1 hour.

Yield: 15 muffins

D
E
S
S
E
R
T
S

Cal 108   Fat 3 g

Oat Bran Banana-Raisin Muffins

Oat bran is available in the cereal section in most supermarkets. It is an excellent source of the kind of fiber that helps to lower blood cholesterol; wheat bran doesn't have the same cholesterol-lowering effect.

Ingredients

1 egg, lightly beaten
3 Tbsp. vegetable oil
½ cup granulated sugar
½ cup 2% milk
1 cup mashed bananas
1 tsp. vanilla

1 cup whole wheat flour
1 tsp. baking soda
1 tsp. baking powder
1 cup oat bran
½ cup raisins

Yield: 12 muffins

Directions

In bowl, combine egg, oil, sugar, 2% milk, bananas and vanilla; mix well.

In another bowl, mix together flour, baking soda, baking powder, oat bran and raisins; stir into egg mixture, mixing only until combined. Spoon into 12 nonstick or paper-lined muffin tins, filling each about ⅔ full. Bake in 400° oven for 20 to 25 minutes or until firm to the touch.

DESSERTS

Cal 165   Fat 4 g

Citrus Bran Muffins

Ingredients

1 ½ cups whole wheat flour
½ cup oat bran
⅓ cup granulated sugar
1 tsp. each baking powder and
    baking soda
¼ tsp. salt

1 cup buttermilk
¼ cup vegetable oil
1 egg, slightly beaten
Grated rinds of ½ lemon and ½
    orange
½ cup chopped dates, prunes or
    raisins

1 Tbsp. sesame seeds

Directions

Combine flour, oat bran, sugar, baking powder, baking soda and salt in large bowl.

Blend together, buttermilk, oil, egg and citrus rinds; stir into dry ingredients just until moistened. Stir in dates.

Spoon batter into 12 lightly greased or paper lined muffin cups. Sprinkle with sesame seeds. Bake in 375° oven 20 minutes or until tops spring back when lightly touched. Remove from pans; cool completely.

Yield: Makes 12 muffins

DESSERTS

Cal 170   Fat 6.2 g

Bran Muffins

One of Cathi's favourites!

Ingredients

1 cup whole wheat flour
¼ cup sugar or molasses
2½ tsp. baking powder
½ tsp. baking soda
½ tsp. salt

1¼ cups 100% bran cereal
1 cup 1% milk

2 egg whites
3 Tbsp. vegetable oil
1 tsp. vanilla

½ cup raisins (optional)

Directions

Combine flour, sugar, baking powder, baking soda and salt. Set aside.

Stir together bran and milk, let stand 5 minutes.

Add egg, oil and vanilla beating well until blended. Add flour mixture stirring just until combined, don't over beat.

Stir in raisins if using. Fill muffin tins ⅔ full. Bake at 400° for 20 minutes.

Yield: 18 large muffins

DESSERTS

Cal 145

Fat 5.2 g

Buttermilk Bran Muffins

Ingredients

2 cups All Bran
4 cups buttermilk
3 eggs
3 tsp. salt
4 cups raisin bran
2 cups boiling water
1½ cups apple juice
2½ cups unsweetened applesauce
4 tsp. soda
5 cups whole wheat flour

Directions

Combine all ingredients in a large bowl. Beat until mixture will thicken. Can be kept in refrigerator for 2 months. Bake at 350° about 20 minutes.

**Yield: Makes 4 to 5
   dozen muffins**

This recipe submitted by Vivian Saccucci.

DESSERTS

Cal 145   Fat 0.4 g

Bran Muffins #2

Ingredients

¼ cup yogurt (plain)
½ tsp. baking soda

1 banana
2 tsp. baking powder
1 tsp. molasses

¾ cup bran
2 eggs
1 tsp. vanilla
4 packages artificial sweetener
½ cup skim milk powder
1 tsp. cinnamon

Yield: 12 muffins

Directions

Dissolve soda in yogurt.

Mash banana and mix with baking powder. Add molasses.

Add bran and remaining ingredients. Pour in muffin tins and bake at 350° for 20 to 25 minutes.

This recipe submitted by Linda Abramenko.

DESSERTS

Cal 70   Fat 0.5 g

Raisin Muffins

Very moist!

Ingredients

1 cup bran cereal
1 cup quick-cooking rolled oats
½ cup raisins
1¾ cups 1% milk

½ cup firmly packed brown
    sugar
⅓ cup margarine, melted
1 egg
1 Tbsp. molasses

1 cup all-purpose white flour
½ cup whole wheat flour
1 Tbsp. baking powder
1 tsp. ground ginger
½ tsp. ground cinnamon
Dash salt

Directions

Combine cereal, oats, raisins and milk; let stand 5 minutes. Stir in sugar, margarine, egg and molasses.

Combine flours, baking powder and seasonings in large bowl. Add cereal mixture to dry ingredients, stirring just until moistened. Spoon into 12 large lightly greased or paper lined muffin cups generously filling to the top. Bake in 400° oven about 20 minutes or until golden brown. Remove from pans; cool completely. Store in an airtight container. These muffins freeze well. This is a healthy moist muffin for breakfast on the run.

Yield: Makes 24 muffins

DESSERTS

Cal 109   Fat 3.6 g

Pineapple Oat Bran Muffins
M I C R O W A V E A B L E

Ingredients

2¼ cups oat bran
1 cup whole-wheat flour
½ tsp. baking soda
¼ cup firmly packed brown
   sugar
2 tsp. baking powder
2 (8-oz.) cans crushed pineapple
   with juice, drained and
   reserve at least ½ cup
¼ cup skim milk
2 egg whites
2 Tbsp. vegetable oil

Cinnamon/sugar mixture or
   finely chopped nuts

Yield: 30 muffins

Directions

Mix oat bran, flour, baking soda, sugar and baking powder in medium bowl. Drain pineapple well, reserving ½ cup juice. Combine juice, milk, egg whites and oil in a bowl. Add to dry ingredients and mix until moistened. Stir in well-drained pineapple. Line muffin pans with double paper liners. Fill to top with batter as muffins do not rise much

Sprinkle tops with cinnamon/sugar mixture or chopped nuts. Microwave on high 3-4 minutes, until moist but not wet. After cooling, store in plastic bag(s). Refrigerate or freeze.

DESSERTS

Cal 138

Fat 1 g

Cinnamon Rolls

Ingredients

3¼ cups all purpose white flour
1 Tbsp. quick-rise instant yeast
¼ cup sugar
½ tsp. salt

¾ cup 1% milk
¼ cup water
½ cup soft margarine, divided

1 egg, lightly beaten
½ cup firmly packed brown
    sugar
1 Tbsp. ground cinnamon
½ cup raisins

Yield: Makes 12 rolls

Directions

Reserve 1 cup flour. Mix remaining flour, yeast, sugar and salt in large bowl.

Heat milk, water and ¼ cup margarine until hot to touch, (125°). Stir hot liquid into dry ingredients.

Stir in egg. Mix in enough reserved flour to make a soft dough that does not stick to bowl. Turn out onto a lightly floured board; knead until smooth and elastic, about 5 minutes. Cover, let rest 10 minutes. Roll dough to a 14-inch square. Spread remaining margarine.

Combine brown sugar and cinnamon; sprinkle over dough with raisins. Roll up dough; pinch seam to seal; cut into 12 slices.

CONTINUED NEXT PAGE

D
E
S
S
E
R
T
S

Cal 271   Fat 8.8 g

Place in greased large muffin cups or rectangular baking pan. Cover, let rise in warm draft-free place until doubled in size, about 30 minutes. Bake in 375° oven about 20 minutes or until brown. Remove from pans to wire rack to cool. Serve warm.

DESSERTS

Whole Wheat Rolls

Ingredients

2 cups all purpose white flour
2 cups whole wheat flour
2 Tbsp. sugar
1 tsp. salt
1 Tbsp. quick rise instant yeast

1 cup 2% milk
½ cup water
3 Tbsp. soft margarine

Directions

Reserve 1 cup all purpose flour. Mix remaining flours, sugar, salt and yeast in large bowl.

Heat milk, water and margarine until hot to touch, (125°). Stir hot liquid into dry ingredients. Mix in enough reserved flour to make a soft dough that does not stick to bowl. Turn out onto a lightly floured board; knead until smooth and elastic, about 8 minutes. Cover; let rest 10 minutes. Shape into 24 rolls. Place on lightly greased baking sheet. Cover; let rise in warm draft-free place until doubled in size, about 40 minutes. Bake in 375° oven about 15 minutes until golden.

Yield: Makes 24 rolls

DESSERTS

Cal 104   Fat 2.8 g

Raspberry Oatmeal Bar Cookies

Ingredients

½ cup room-temperature margarine
½ cup light-brown sugar
1 cup flour
¼ tsp. baking soda
Dash of salt
1 cup rolled oats
¾ cup fruit-only seedless raspberry jam

Directions

Heat the oven to 350°. Grease an 8" square pan, line it with aluminum foil and then grease the foil. Combine all the ingredients except the jam. Press 2 cups of the mixture into the bottom of the pan. Spread the jam to within ¼ inch of the edge. Sprinkle the remaining crumb mixture over the top and lightly press it into the jam. Bake 35 to 40 minutes and allow to cool on a wire rack before cutting.

Yield: 24 2 × 1½ inch bars

DESSERTS

Cal 103

Fat 4 g

Morning Cookies

Ingredients

4 ripe medium-size bananas,
   mashed
⅓ cup vegetable oil
1 tsp. vanilla extract
Grated rind of 1 orange

1½ cups quick rolled oats
1½ cups chopped mixed dried
   fruit (raisins, apricots, dates,
   prunes)
¾ cup whole wheat flour
½ cup coarsely chopped
   almonds(optional)

Directions

In large bowl, mash bananas and
stir in oil, vanilla and orange
rind.

Combine oats, fruit, flour and
(almonds); stir into bananas until
blended. Drop by small spoonfuls onto lightly greased baking
sheets. Flatten with a fork. Bake
in a 350° oven about 20 minutes or until lightly browned.
Immediately remove from pan,
cool completely; store in refrigerator.

Yield: Makes 48 cookies

Cal 52   Fat 1.8 g

DESSERTS

Carob Cookies

Ingredients

1½ cups whole wheat flour
½ cup carob powder
1 cup powdered milk
2½ cups unsweetened applesauce
¼ cup water
1 tsp. baking powder
1 tsp. salt
6 egg whites
1 Tbsp. vanilla

Directions

Mix all the ingredients together. Bake in a 9" x 13" pan at 325° for 35 minutes.

Yield: 36 cookies

This recipe submitted by Vivian Saccucci.

Calories and fat per cookie.

DESSERTS

Cal 36   Fat "tr"

Wheat Germ Cookies

Ingredients

1 cup brown sugar
2 Tbsp. soy flour
4 Tbsp. wheat germ flakes
¼ tsp. salt
1 tsp. vanilla
½ cup soft diet margarine
½ cup whole wheat flour
½ cup chopped nuts or fruit

Directions

Mix ingredients well in order given. Drop on non-stick sprayed and floured pan. Bake 20 to 25 minutes at 375°.
Note: A little grated orange rind gives a nice flavour.

This recipe submitted by Vivian Saccucci.

Calories and fat per cookie.

**Yield: approx.
24 cookies**

D
E
S
S
E
R
T
S

Cal 78   Fat 2.25 g

Meringue Cookies

Ingredients

3 egg whites
Pinch of cream of tartar or
    lemon
¾ cup white sugar
½ tsp. vanilla

Optional: 1 cup almonds (slivered)

Directions

Whip egg whites 30 seconds. Add cream of tartar or lemon. Whip until stiff. Add sugar ¾ tablespoon at a time and then add vanilla. Fold in almonds if desired. Place 2 layers of wax paper or a brown paper bag on cookie sheet. Drop on by spoonfuls. Place in oven for 1 hour at 275° then turn off oven and let them cool in oven.

This recipe submitted by Vivian Saccucci.

Calories and fat per cookie

Yield: 20 - 24 cookies

Cal 45   Fat 1.2 g

Light Brownies

Ingredients

2 cups whole wheat flour
1½ cups sugar
6 Tbsp. cocoa
¼ cup light margarine, melted
¾ cup applesauce
8 egg whites
1 tsp. vanilla
½ cup walnuts, chopped

Frosting:
¾ cup sugar
2 Tbsp. cocoa
1 tsp. light corn syrup
2 Tbsp. water
1 egg white
1 tsp. vanilla

Directions

Preheat oven to 350°. Grease a brownie pan with non-stick spray. Combine the dry ingredients. Add melted margarine and applesauce. Batter will be crumbly. In a separate bowl beat egg whites until stiff; stir into batter. Add vanilla; fold in walnuts. Pour into pan. Bake for 20 to 23 minutes.

In a double boiler mix all the frosting ingredients, except for the vanilla, and beat with hand mixer for one minute. Set over boiling water, beating for four to five minutes until thick. Remove from heat, continuing to beat until thick enough to spread. Add vanilla and mix. For easy spreading, frost brownies while they are still warm. Also, if you frost the brownies while they are warm, you will use less frosting.

Yield: 40 2-inch brownies

D
E
S
S
E
R
T
S

Cal 87   Fat 1 g

Chocolate Carrot Cake

MICROWAVEABLE

Ingredients

1¼ cups all purpose flour with
   wheat bran
¾ cup firmly packed brown
   sugar
⅓ cup cocoa
1 tsp. baking soda
½ tsp. each ground cinnamon
   and nutmeg
¼ cup vegetable oil
¼ cup pineapple juice, unsweetened
2 eggs
1 tsp. vanilla extract

1½ cups shredded carrot
½ cup well drained, crushed
   pineapple, unsweetened

Yield: 9 servings

Directions

Combine flour, brown sugar, cocoa, baking soda, cinnamon, nutmeg, oil, juice, eggs and vanilla in large bowl. Beat together with electric mixer on low speed until well blended; scrape bowl occasionally.

Stir in carrots and drained pineapple. Spread batter evenly in lightly greased 9 inch microwave safe tube pan. Microwave at High (100%), uncovered, 8 to 9 minutes or until tooth-pick inserted in centre comes out clean. Rotate pan ¼ turn every 2 minutes during cooking. Let stand on counter-top for 10 minutes. Loosen edges; turn out onto serving platter. Let cool completely.

DESSERTS

Cal 241   Fat 8.7 g

Pound Cake

Ingredients

½ cup applesauce
½ cup nonfat milk
1 tsp. vanilla

2¾ cups flour
2 tsp. baking powder

8 egg whites
1½ cups sugar

Optional: 3½ tsp. almond
extract

Yield: 1 loaf

Directions

Grease a tube pan with vegetable-oil spray, and flour it. In a mixing bowl, combine applesauce, milk, vanilla and extract; set aside.

In a second bowl, combine flour and baking powder, and set aside also.

In a third bowl, beat egg whites until foamy; gradually add sugar and beat until stiff peaks form. Alternately drizzle milk mixture and sprinkle flour mixture into egg foam, and fold in. Pour batter into tube pan. Bake at 350° for 50 to 55 minutes. Immediately invert cake, still in pan. Cool thoroughly. Gently loosen sides of cake and remove it from pan.

DESSERTS

Cal 155   Fat 0.8 g

Angel Food Cake

Ingredients

1 cup cake and pastry flour
1 cup granulated sugar

1 ½ cups egg whites, about 11
   large egg whites
1 ½ tsp. cream of tartar
½ tsp. salt
1 tsp. vanilla

Yield: 12 servings

Directions

Preheat oven to 350° and have an ungreased 10-inch tube pan ready to hold batter. Measure flour, then ¼ cup sugar into a medium-size bowl. Stir with a fork until evenly blended. Set aside.

Measure egg whites, cream of tartar, salt and vanilla into a large mixing bowl. Beat with an electric mixer at high speed until soft peaks form when beaters are lifted, about 5 to 6 minutes. Then gradually beat in remaining 3/4 cup sugar. Beat until stiff shiny peaks form when beaters are lifted. Then sift about one-quarter of flour mixture over beaten egg whites. Using a large spatula, gently fold together. Repeat this process with remaining flour mixture. (It's not necessary to fold in flour completely until last addition).

CONTINUED NEXT PAGE

DESSERTS

Cal 117

Fat < 1 g

Turn batter into ungreased tube pan. Using a knife, cut through batter several times to remove any air bubbles. Bake in centre of preheated oven for 40 to 45 minutes or until cake springs back when lightly touched. Remove from oven and turn pan upside down on a rack or heat-proof counter. Let cake cool in pan. When cool, run a knife around edges and remove cake from pan. Cool completely. Cover and store in the refrigerator if not using right away. Serve with Strawberry Yogurt Sauce.

DESSERTS

Yogurt Fruit Sauce

Ingredients

1 ½ cups fresh or unsweetened
  frozen fruit or 1 cup frozen
  fruit in light syrup (strawberries, blueberries, etc.)

½ cup plain low-fat yogurt
1 Tbsp. granulated sugar
  (optional)

Directions

Place fresh or frozen berries in a
food processor. Whirl, using an
on- and off- motion, until
coarsely pureed.

Mix in yogurt. Taste. Add sugar,
if you wish.

Yield: Makes 1 ½ cups

DESSERTS

Cal 33   Fat 1 g

"Cheesecake" (Tofu)

Ingredients

8 oz. tofu, pressed
Sweetener to taste
½ tsp. vanilla
One 12-oz. can diet cream
    soda, heated
1 envelope gelatin (dissolve in ⅓
    cup water)

Directions

Put in blender: tofu, sweetener and vanilla. Blend well while slowly pouring in the cream soda. Add the gelatin-water mixture. Blend 1 minute. Pour into a 1 quart casserole sprayed with non-stick spray. Refrigerate 2 hours or up to 3 days. If storing longer than 2 hours; cover tightly with plastic film.

Optional Fruit Topping

In a small saucepan, combine 1 cup blueberries with ½ cup water and sweetener to taste. Dissolve 1 package gelatin in ⅓ cup water. Remove the fruit from the stove and stir in the gelatin. Refrigerate. When almost set (stir after 15 minutes), spread the fruit mixture over the "cheesecake."

Yield: 4 servings

DESSERTS

Cal 50   Fat 2 g

Quick Cake

Ingredients

3 eggs
Pinch of salt
1 cup sugar
1 cup flour
1 tsp. vanilla

Directions

Separate eggs; put whites into a deep glass mixing bowl with a pinch of salt. Beat well with beater. Add sugar, beating steadily; add egg yolks. Continue beating until very light. Add flour, folding in with heavy spoon; then vanilla. Pour into 8 inch square, non-stick coated pan. Bake for 20 minutes at 350°

Yield: 16 servings

This recipe submitted by Vivian Saccucci.

DESSERTS

Cal 91

Fat 0.6 g

No-Fat Frosting!

Ingredients

1 egg white, chilled
¾ cup white sugar
¼ tsp. cream of tartar
Pinch of salt
½ tsp. vanilla

½ cup boiling water

Directions

Put all ingredients in bowl then pour ½ cup boiling water in and beat till it stands in peaks and is fluffy. Delicious!

This recipe submitted by Vivian Saccucci.

Total calories.

Yield: 8" square cake

Cal 586   Fat 0 g

Whole Wheat Pastry

Ingredients

1 cup whole wheat flour
½ tsp. salt
½ tsp. baking powder

4 Tbsp. shortening
3-4 Tbsp. ice cold water

**Yield: Makes 1
9-inch pastry shell**

Directions

Combine flour, salt and baking powder.

Cut in shortening with 2 knives or pastry blender until mixture resembles coarse meal with a few larger pieces. Gradually add ice water, 1 Tbsp. at a time, to make dough hold together. Press into ball.

Roll dough, on lightly floured board, from centre outward, with a light, even pressure to form a 10". Roll pastry over rolling pin, do not stretch; fit carefully into 9" pie plate. Trim and flute edge. Generously prick bottom and sides with a fork.

Conventional Oven – Bake in 450° oven for 10 to 12 minutes.

Microwave: – Let pastry rest 10 minutes in the pie plate before cooking. Microwave at High (100%) 3½ to 5 minutes. Pastry is opaque when done.

DESSERTS

Cal 844   Fat 53.7

Low-Fat Pie Shell

N O S H O R T E N I N G !

Ingredients

½ cup whole wheat flour
⅛ tsp. salt
1 Tbsp. oil
4 Tbsp. cold water

Directions

Mix all together in order given. Knead until pastry forms a ball. Chill well in refrigerator before rolling out on a lightly floured board. Place in a 9 inch pie pan. Prick the bottom in several places with a fork and quick brown in a 425° oven about 10 minutes.

Yield: 1 9" shell

Calories and fat per shell:

D E S S E R T S

Cal 490   Fat 15.6 g

Graham Pie Crust

Ingredients

For One Pie:
1 ¼ cups Graham cracker crumbs
2 Tbsp. melted margarine
¼ cup brown sugar
1 Tbsp. warm water
½ tsp. cinnamon

Directions

Mix ingredients together and press into 8 or 9" pie plate. Bake at 300° for 5 to 8 minutes. Refrigerate.

Pie Decorations
After baking with filling of your choice, use fresh fruit to make a pleasing design on top of your pies. Make circles and scalloped circular patterns with the edge of the sliced fruit. Use raisins for the centre of the pattern, if desired.

**D
E
S
S
E
R
T
S**

Yield: 1 8" or 9" shell

Calories and fat per shell:

Cal 661

Fat 18.5 g

Pie Fillings

Use fruits that are in season whenever possible. Mash, grate or slice. Use your imagination in food combinations.

Apple

Ingredients
8 grated Pipin or Cortland
    apples
2 chopped apples
1 lemon sliced
1 tsp. honey or 1 Tbsp. date
    sugar
2 Tbsp. raisins

Directions
Mix all ingredients together. Spread on crust. Sprinkle top with coconut. Refrigerate.

Blueberry

Ingredients
4 cups blueberries
1 Tbsp. honey or maple syrup
    (optional)
1 Tbsp. lemon juice

Directions
Mash or blend ingredients together. Spread on crust. Decorate the top. Refrigerate.

DESSERTS

Cal 543   Fat 3.2 g   Cal 392   Fat 2.4 g

Yummie Balls

Nutritious and delicious!

Ingredients

½ cup peanut butter
½ cup honey (may put part
   molasses)
¼ cup carob powder
¼ cup wheat germ
½ cup dry powdered milk

Optional: add crushed nuts or
   seeds

1 cup your choice of cereal
   crumbs (corn flakes, rice
   krispies)

Yield: 30 - 36

Directions

Mix ingredients and form into
small balls, then roll in crushed
corn flakes, rice krispies or ?

*This recipe submitted by Vivian
Saccucci.*

Calories and fat without nuts

DESSERTS

Cal 63   Fat 2 g

Divinity Fudge

Ingredients

1½ cup brown sugar
½ cup water
1 tsp. white vinegar

1 egg white, stiffly beaten
½ tsp. vanilla

Optional: ½ cup walnuts,
almonds or seeds

Yield: 81 1" squares

Directions

Combine brown sugar, water and vinegar in heavy saucepan. Cook over medium heat, stirring constantly until it boils. Cool to 250° without stirring.

Remove from heat and pour over stiffly beaten egg white, beating till thick (5 minutes). Fold in nuts and vanilla. Pour into pan and cut.

This recipe submitted by Vivian Saccucci.

Calories and fat per square without nuts.

D
E
S
S
E
R
T
S

Cal 15   Fat 0 g

Low-Cal Jelly Candy

Less than 500 calories for entire pan. Very chewy. Satisfies that "sweet tooth" without fat or calories!

Ingredients

16 packages of gelatin or 16 Tbsp. unflavoured gelatin from bulk food store
3 packages any flavour jello-light
4 cups boiling water

Directions

Mix jello and gelatin together thoroughly in medium-size bowl. Add boiling water, stirring until well dissolved. Pour in 9" x 13" pan and chill in fridge till set. Can be cut to any size you wish.

This recipe submitted by Vivian Saccucci.

Calories and fat per pan.

Yield: 9 x 13 inch pan

DESSERTS

Cal 450   Fat 0 g

Berry Meringues

Ingredients

4 egg whites, at room temperature
¼ tsp. salt
¼ tsp. cream of tartar

½ cup granulated or fruit sugar
½ tsp. vanilla
2 cups fresh berries, such as strawberries, blueberries or blackberries

Yield: 4 - 6 servings

Directions

Preheat oven to 225° Lightly butter a sheet of waxed paper and dust lightly with cornstarch, shaking off excess. Place on a baking sheet. Prepare meringues by placing room-temperature egg whites in a large mixing bowl. Add salt and cream of tartar. Beat with an electric mixer at high speed until whites will just hold soft moist peaks when beaters are lifted.

Very gradually beat in sugar, 1 tablespoon at a time, at medium speed. Continue to beat until stiff shiny peaks will form. Beat in vanilla. Immediately spoon about half the meringue onto prepared waxed paper. Using the back of a spoon, form into 4 (3-inch) circles, about ⅓ inch thick. Either use remaining meringue to build 1-inch-high borders or to pipe 1-inch-high rosettes, using a piping bag,

CONTINUED NEXT PAGE

DESSERTS

Cal 132   Fat 0 g

around edges. Bake in centre of preheated oven for 1 to 1¼ hours. Turn off oven but leave meringues in oven for at least 1 more hour (preferably overnight). Then slide waxed paper holding meringues onto a rack. Cool meringues completely. To remove from waxed paper, gently slide a sharp knife between paper and meringues. Then peel off carefully. Fill cooled meringues with fresh berries.

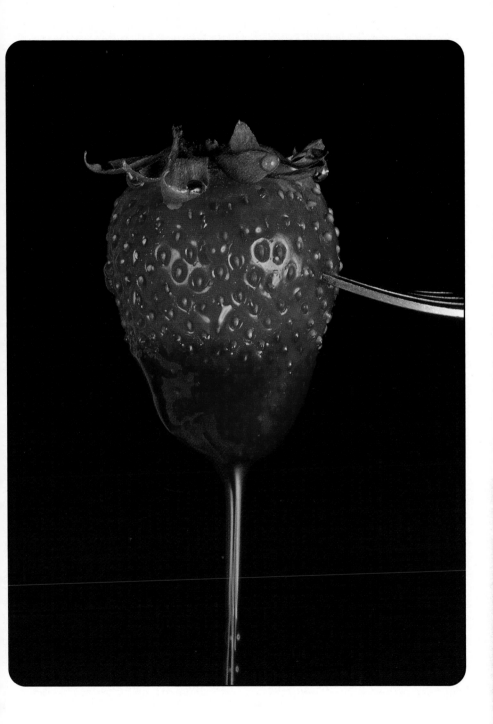

Strawberry Yogurt Mousse

MICROWAVEABLE

Ingredients

⅓ cup orange juice
2 Tbsp. unflavoured gelatin
    (2 envelopes)

1 ½ cups frozen strawberries
½ cup sugar
1 tsp. orange rind
1 cup plain skim yogurt

3 egg whites

Yield: 6 servings

Directions

Combine juice and gelatin in a large pyrex measuring cup. Microwave on Med-High, stirring well for 2-3 minutes until it just begins to boil.

Reserve a few strawberries for garnish. Puree remaining berries with sugar and orange rind. Add dissolved gelatin and blend. Mix in yogurt.

Beat egg whites in a separate bowl till stiff but not dry. Fold into berry mixture. Spoon into a 1 ½ quart serving dish. Refrigerate several hours before serving. Garnish with remaining strawberry slices.

This recipe submitted by Gale Larabee.

DESSERTS

Cal 138   Fat 0.5 g

Easy Lime Cream

Ingredients

1 cup frozen whipped topping
⅓ cup sweetener
½ cup freshly squeezed lime
  juice, about 3 limes
Finely grated peel of 2 limes
Sliced fruit (optional)

Directions

Combine all ingredients, except fruit, in a bowl. Stir until mixture starts to thicken, about 2 minutes. Spoon over fresh fruit or place in freezer until mixture is the consistency of ice cream.

**D
E
S
S
E
R
T
S**

Yield: 4 servings

Cal 81   Fat 2 g

"Fruit Yogurt" (Tofu)

Ingredients

8 oz. tofu, pressed
Sweetener to taste
Dash of cinnamon and nutmeg
¼ cup lemon juice
Mineral water - just enough to
   give mixture consistency of
   yogurt
1 cup frozen blueberries, strawberries, raspberries or
   blackberries

Directions

Put tofu, sweetener, cinnamon, nutmeg and lemon juice in blender and blend until smooth. Add berries and a little mineral water. Blend well and add more mineral water and sweetener if needed.

Yield: 4 servings

DESSERTS

Cal 109   Fat 2.4 g

"Custard Pudding" (Tofu)

Ingredients

10 oz. tofu (lightly pressed)
1 egg
¼ cup lemon juice
1 envelope sweetener
Sweetener to taste
Pinch of Salt
½ tsp. vanilla extract

Directions

Combine all ingredients in blender; blend until smooth. Pour into 6 custard cups. Cover cups with foil and put in steamer. Steam over low heat for 20 to 25 minutes, or until firm. OR: Place cups in a shallow pan with ¾ inch hot water and bake in preheated 325° oven for about 20 minutes. Serve hot or cold.

Yield: 6 servings

D
E
S
S
E
R
T
S

Cal 71   Fat 3 g

Apple Meringue Pudding

Great for apple pie lovers, without the fatty crust. The topping is a great addition that goes especially well with cranberries.

Ingredients

5 apples, peeled, cored and
  chopped (about 6 cups)
1 cup cranberries
½ cup packed brown sugar
2 Tbsp. whole wheat flour
2 tsp. cinnamon

4 egg whites
½ tsp. cream of tartar
⅔ cup granulated sugar
1 tsp. vanilla
Nutmeg (optional)

Yield: 8 servings

Directions

In bowl, combine apples, cranberries, sugar, flour and cinnamon. Spoon into 10-inch pie plate; cover with foil and bake in 325° oven for 20 minutes. (Recipe can be made ahead and refrigerated for up to 1 day; bring to room temperature before proceeding).

In bowl, beat egg whites and cream of tartar until soft peaks form. Gradually beat in sugar until stiff peaks form. Fold in vanilla. Remove cover from fruit; top with meringue, covering fruit completely. Bake in 325° oven for 35 to 40 minutes or until golden brown. Sprinkle with nutmeg if desired. Serve immediately.

DESSERTS

Cal 180   Fat 0.5 g

Rice Tofu Pudding

Ingredients

3 oz. tofu, soft or firm

½ envelope unflavoured gelatin
½ cup water

¼ tsp. ground cinnamon
1 tsp. vanilla extract
1 tsp. vanilla butternut flavour
⅓ cup nonfat dry milk

½ cup cooked white or
   brown rice
2 Tbsp. raisins
Ground cinnamon
Dash of ground nutmeg

Yield: 4 servings

Directions

Slice tofu and drain well between towels.

Sprinkle gelatin over water in a small saucepan and let soften a few minutes. Heat over low heat until gelatin is completely dissolved, stirring frequently.

In a blender container, combine gelatin mixture, tofu, cinnamon, vanilla extract, vanilla butternut flavour and dry milk. Blend until smooth. Pour into a bowl and chill until firm about 45 minutes. Beat chilled pudding on low speed of an electric mixer until smooth.

Stir in rice and raisins and pour mixture into a serving bowl. Sprinkle with cinnamon and dash of nutmeg. Chill.

This recipe submitted by Gale Larabee.

DESSERTS

Cal 184   Fat 1 g

Baked Apples

Ingredients

4 medium tart baking apples

4 tsp. brown sugar
2 tsp. margarine
1 tsp. each of cinnamon and
    nutmeg

Directions

Preheat oven to 375°. Hollow core out of each apple, leaving about 1 inch of core at bottom.

Combine remaining ingredients and fill centres of apples with mixture. Place apples in shallow pan or casserole with ¼ inch boiling water. Cover and bake 40 to 50 minutes, until tender. Serve warm or chilled.

Yield: 4 servings

DESSERTS

Cal 115   Fat 2 g

Prune Jam

Ingredients

¾ cup dried pitted prunes
½ cup orange juice

Directions

Blenderize prunes in orange juice until thick and creamy (for more orange juice flavour use frozen concentrate instead of juice.

This recipe submitted by Vivian Saccucci.

Calories and fat per ounce:

Yield: 12 oz.

D
E
S
S
E
R
T
S

Cal 32   Fat 0 g

Fig Jam

Ingredients

2 oranges
1 cup apple juice
2 cups dried figs

Optional: 1 cup honey
Optional: 1 tsp. cinnamon

Directions

In blender put oranges, apple juice and ½ of the figs and blend till smooth, continue adding rest of figs and blending till smooth.

This jam can be eaten as is or cooked. If you cook it you have to add the honey. Simmer and stir often. Frozen apple concentrate can be used if a stronger flavour is desired instead of the juice. Can be frozen.

Yield: 4 cups

This recipe submitted by Vivian Saccucci.

DESSERTS

Cal 47   Fat 0 g

Low-Cal Whole Wheat Breakfast Cakes

Ingredients

1 ¼ cup whole wheat flour
2 ¼ tsp. baking powder
¼ tsp. salt

1 egg
1 ¼ cups skim milk
Non-stick vegetable cooking
   spray

Yield: 8 servings

Directions

Combine flour, baking powder and salt in mixing bowl.

Beat together egg and milk, and stir into flour mixture to form a lumpy batter, spray non-stick pan with cooking spray and heat over medium heat. Drop batter by spoonfuls onto pan to make 4-inch pancakes. Reduce heat to low and cook until bubbles begin to form on cakes. Turn and cook on the other side until golden brown.

This recipe submitted by Linda Abramenko.

DESSERTS

Cal 87

Fat 0.8 g

Low-Cal Sugarless Pancake Syrup

Ingredients

1 Tbsp. cornstarch
2 Tbsp. cold water
1 cup boiling water

2 Tbsp. butter or margarine
¾ tsp. maple flavouring
Few grains of salt
Sugar substitute to equal ½ cup
    sugar

Directions

Blend cornstarch with cold water, add boiling water and boil 5 minutes, stirring constantly until smooth.

Remove from heat and add butter, maple flavour, salt and sugar substitute. Store in fridge. Warm before serving.

Yield: 12 oz.

This recipe submitted by Linda Abramenko.

DESSERTS

Cal 17   Fat 1 g

Tofu Pancakes

Ingredients

6 oz. tofu, unpressed
1 egg
2 Tbsp. unprocessed bran
¼ cup water
Seasonings from variations
   below

Variations: The taste of the pancakes is determined by the seasonings. Try one of these combinations, or create your own.
1. Cinnamon, cloves, Nutra Sweet and allspice
2. Italian Seasoning, garlic powder, onion powder, oregano and black pepper
3. Red chili powder, cumin, garlic powder and black pepper
4. Curry, garlic powder, turmeric and black pepper
5. Ginger, soy sauce and garlic powder

Yield: 8 servings

Directions

Combine all ingredients in blender container. Blend until very smooth, 2-4 minutes. Cook in preheated non-stick pan, over medium heat, until bubbles form and break. Turn carefully, cook 2 minutes on other side.

Calories and fat based on basic recipe.

DESSERTS

Cal 23   Fat 1 g

Banana Milkshakes

Ingredients

2½ cups frozen banana chunks
1 cup skim milk
1 tsp. vanilla

Version #1: Add ½ tsp. honey and ⅛ tsp. maple extract

Version #2: Add 1 Tbsp. carob powder and 1 Tbsp. plain malted milk powder

Directions

Combine ingredients together in a blender. Serve chilled.

This recipe submitted by Vivian Saccucci.

Calories and fat with carob and malt.

Yield: 3 cups

Cal 175   Fat 1 g

Banana-Orange Punch

Ingredients

4 cups skim or 1% milk
Frozen orange juice concentrate
1½ cups water
3 bananas

Yield: 6 cups

Directions

Whip milk and orange juice in blender (partially dilute concentrate with 1½ cups water). Add bananas and whip till frothy. If you like it sweeter you can add artificial sweetener.

This recipe submitted by Vivian Saccucci.

DESSERTS

Cal 133   Fat 1.6 g

Chocolate Drizzle

Ingredients

2 tsp. unsweetened cocoa
1 tsp. granulated sugar
1 tsp. cornstarch

½ cup evaporated 2% milk
⅛ tsp. vanilla extract

2 cups (approx. 1 lb.) berries or
fruit of your choice

Directions

In a small saucepan combine cocoa, sugar and cornstarch into ¼ cup of the evaporated milk. Heat mixture and stir until sugar is completely dissolved.

Add remaining milk and vanilla. Cook over medium heat, stirring constantly until mixture comes to a boil. Reduce heat and continue to stir until thick (about 2 minutes. Remove from heat.

Pour chocolate sauce into measuring cup and let cool. Cover with plastic wrap and refrigerate until chilled. Drizzle sauce over fruit or berries that have been spaced out on plate.

**Yield: 4 oz. per lb.
        of fruit**

DESSERTS

Cal 84   Fat 2.6 g